"The world is a book and those who do not travel read only one page."

St. Augustine

ⓡ QUINTESSENTIALLY RESERVE

Welcome to the inaugural edition of Quintessentially Reserve, a new collection of the world's leading luxury retreats, from city hotels to safari lodges, from spa resorts to private boltholes. We have covered the world for you, from Africa to New York, from London to the farthest reaches of Latin America. A guide that will be produced annually for your pleasure, Quintessentially Reserve features many of the stalwart properties in the luxury travel sector as well as lesser-known, less-expected gems that we would like you to discover and enjoy.

For more information about the participating properties, you can visit the website at www.quintessentiallyreserve.com.

We would also like to receive your feedback, to share your thoughts and recommendations on Quintessentially Reserve's collection with future readers. Please email qreserve@quintessentially.com.

I sincerely hope you enjoy the book, and more importantly, that you take some time out and get on a plane.

Liam Wholey
Director

"If you actually look like your passport photo, you aren't well enough to travel."

Sir Vivian Fuchs

Europe

 *Palais Coburg* RESIDENZ

When the Palais Coburg Residenz – headed by the General Manager Jan Hendrik Van Dillen – opened in 2003, it met Vienna's crying need for a five-star, all-suite address in a city packed with traditional hotels. It strikes a happy balance between old and new, the fresh, modern, 35 suites occupying a late Neo-Classical/Early Historicist building in the city centre (note the portico with its freestanding columns; it's what led the Palais to be given the affectionate nickname, the 'Spargelburg' or 'castle of asparagus'). Suites are capacious, sized from 54 to 160 square metres. Furnishings are gently contemporary and easy on the eye with soft neutrals bathed in natural light. Banqueting facilities are among the best in town (up to 500 people) and the spa has a pool, sauna, steam and gym.

QUINTESSENTIALLY INSIDER

Be sure to make a reservation at the Restaurant Coburg – the city's sole member of Relais & Châteaux – from Christian Petz, Austria's former 'Cook of The Year'. Dishes showcase his purist style. Menus also feature classics from the Viennese kitchen.

Palais Coburg Residenz   Tel: +43 1 518 18 0
Coburgbastei 4   Fax: +43 1 518 18 100
1010 Vienna   Email: hotel.residenz@palais-coburg.com
Austria   Web: www.palais-coburg.com

Hotel Imperial

Vienna | Austria

Vienna's Hotel Imperial dates from 1863 as the private residence of the Prince of Württemberg. Transformed into a hotel for the Universal Exhibition in 1873, it has long been among Europe's most glamorous addresses. Tasteful furnishings, marble bathrooms, high stucco-adorned ceilings, silk walls, antiques and chandeliers all contribute to an inimitable atmosphere belonging to 19th-century Vienna. Except you've got modern technology and seamless service (even the newspaper is hand-ironed, brought to your bedside with morning tea). The Restaurant Imperial offers traditional Austrian specialities. Café Imperial is well known for the Imperial Torte. Bar Maria Theresia has live piano music in stylish, wood-panelled surroundings.

QUINTESSENTIALLY INSIDER

Sure, the paintings are all originals, but expect more from the Imperial's butler-serviced suites. Try for size the Maisonette Suite, and the views from your own private balcony over the spires of old Vienna.

Hotel Imperial
Kärntner Ring 16
1015 Vienna
Austria

Tel: +43 1 501 100
Fax: +43 1 501 10 410
Email: hotel.imperial@luxurycollection.com
Web: www.luxurycollection.com/imperial

Almyra

Pafos | Cyprus

If only all out-of-date hotels got the Almyra treatment. This remodelled, 158-room privately-owned resort used to be the Pafos Beach Hotel on Cyprus. Now it's where knowing families go for their summer holidays, smug in the decision they've plumped for the right location smack on the water yet only minutes away from the old town of Pafos. For real value for money, they're getting contemporary style and child-friendly facilities (including a pool for the little ones, a kids' club and playground). It's a simple combination that just works, while the accommodation – including the 'Kyma' suites with a private rooftop terrace right on the seafront – gives everyone space to breathe in the mayhem of holidaying en famille.

QUINTESSENTIALLY INSIDER

Don't even think about eating out. At the Almyra, you've got one of the best restaurants on the island – Notios, serving a mix of Mediterranean and Japanese cuisines for which non-residents fight for tables. In summer, there's a beach eatery, Ouzeri, for light Greek delicacies.

Almyra
P.O. Box 60136
CY-8125 Pafos
Cyprus
Tel: +357 26 888 700
Fax: +357 26 942 818
Email: almyra@thanoshotels.com
Web: www.thanoshotels.com

Anassa

When the Anassa first arrived on Cyprus in the late 1990s, it rocked the Med – a fresh, modern, five-star beach resort that moved beyond the region's sprawling new-builds. It also opened a Thalassa Spa that beat the French at their own game (thalassotherapy, or seawater therapy, is why Biarritz girls don't get cellulite – or so they say). You know you're in Greece for the architecture speaks of the island's Byzantine roots. It's totally spoiling, with Emperor-sized villas and suites, some with private plunge pools and whirlpools on sea-facing terraces. There's a surfeit of facilities – a PADI dive school, 15 powerboats, jet-skis, a yacht for cruising the Akamas Peninsula, tennis courts, squash, a kids' club and four restaurants.

QUINTESSENTIALLY INSIDER

The Anassa has an edge on the Mediterranean competition: it's warm down here, making the resort a popular off-season bolthole. In December, balmy days are ideal for rock climbing, hill trekking or diving in the Akamas Marine Reserve. The girlfriends/wives will be more than happy with the spa, tennis coach and fat-fighting menus.

Anassa
P.O. Box 66006
CY-8830 Polis
Cyprus
Tel: +357 26 888 000
Fax: +357 26 322 900
Email: res.anassa@thanoshotels.com
Web: www.thanoshotels.com

The Clubhouse

Chamonix was crying out for somewhere like The Clubhouse, a boutique hotel and members' bar that throws off the Haute Savoie's weighty mantle of pinewood and dirndls. Contemporary and indulgent, The Clubhouse is for mountain lovers in both winter and summer, for skiing, snowboarding, hiking and whitewater rafting. Regarded as the most exciting of the Alpine resorts, Chamonix attracts adrenaline-seekers with an extreme sense of fun (suffice to say Chamonix boasts the world's longest off-piste run, the legendary Vallée Blanche). You can guess the vibe at The Clubhouse Bar, sister to London's Milk & Honey. Accommodation ranges from the Myla Suite with its vast, custom-made bed, to cosy bunkhouse rooms-to-share. All feature teak-decked 'rainforest' showers, flatscreen TVs, DVD players and Frette linen. The Kumari Room is the place for a massage.

QUINTESSENTIALLY INSIDER

You'll want to stay at The Clubhouse just for access to the Bar, otherwise confined to members. Among the hippest hangouts in the Alps, it does great food, fabulous parties and a few very rare Armagnacs.

The Clubhouse
74 Promenade des Sonnailles
Chamonix-Mont Blanc
France 74400

Tel: +33 4 50 90 96 56
Fax: +33 4 50 90 82 49
Email: stay@clubhouse.fr
Web: www.clubhouse.fr

Grand-Hôtel du Cap-Ferrat

Côte d'Azur | France

Grand-Hôtel du Cap-Ferrat is one of those Côte d'Azur addresses that's rich in myth. And little wonder. There's the dream location on the tip of the Cap-Ferrat peninsula. The architecture is classic Belle Epoque – what we all want of this glamorous, Gatsby-esque neck-of-the-woods – and flanked by 15 acres of gardens and pinewood. The pool is the pièce de resistance: infinity-edged, Olympic-sized and stretching into the horizon with sundecks, loungers, a bar and casual buffet restaurant. Jean-Claude Guillon heads up 'Le Cap', the hotel's gourmet fixture, which in July and August features an orchestra and fireworks on the terraces. Enjoy it if you can. Reservations at Grand-Hôtel du Cap-Ferrat are hard to secure – there are just 53 rooms and suites – so call way before the season begins.

QUINTESSENTIALLY INSIDER

The hotel has just unveiled its new Beauty Care concept at the Salon Caravelle with Zen-style facilities. Take it from Q: if French beauty treatments are among the best in the world, then here you've got therapists who practice on royalty.

Grand-Hôtel du Cap-Ferrat
71 Boulevard du Général de Gaulle
06230 Saint-Jean Cap-Ferrat
France

Tel: +33 4 93 76 50 50
Fax: +33 4 93 76 04 52
Email: reserv@grand-hotel-cap-ferrat.com
Web: www.grand-hotel-cap-ferrat.com

Les Deux Abbesses

Les Deux Abbesses has a refreshingly original approach to luxury. It's all about the location, hidden away in a tiny French village built of basalt rock between two quiet rivers, a 60-minute drive from Clermont Ferrand airport deep in the Auvergne. The main castle originally dates from the 12th century, latterly renovated by two 16th-century abbesses. Now it is in the hands of Laurence Perceval-Hermet, who also creates all meals, using herbs picked that morning from the castle's gardens. Accommodation consists of 12 rooms, or rather village cottages, each patiently restored and uniquely decorated. The love and attention is conspicuous: specially commissioned sheets made by an old French factory, embroidered bath linen, the cashmere brush that lies in your armoire.

QUINTESSENTIALLY INSIDER

Les Deux Abbesses is deeply romantic (Q recommends La Grange, a dream-like rural loft with four-poster bed). Be sure to book massage treatments in advance of your stay.

Les Deux Abbesses
Le Château
43300 Saint-Arcons d'Allier
France
Tel: +33 4 71 74 03 08
Fax: +33 4 71 74 05 30
Email: abbesses@relaischateaux.com
Web: www.lesdeuxabbesses.com

Hotel Montalembert

The Hotel Montalembert set the world alight when it opened in 1990, a 56-room 'boutique hotel' delivering contemporary style in addition to cosy intimacy and high-class service. Still it retains its appeal, the timelessness of the original 1926 architecture combined with cool whites and taupes, warming woods and Cascais marble. The location is well-nigh perfect, in the heart of Saint-Germain-des-Prés, home of art galleries and some of the city's best shopping. The Musée d'Orsay and Louvre are within a five-minute walk. Eat in the lounge with its fireplace, the private Salon Gallimard, on the streetside terrace, or at Rive Gauche, the headline restaurant. The bar and 'Tea Time' bustles with chi-chi locals (even if you're not staying, the Montalembert is always a great place to meet).

QUINTESSENTIALLY INSIDER

Junior Suites tend to go first at the Montalembert. They're all located on the eighth floor with pretty attic-style mansards creating a typical Parisian atmosphere. At 25 square metres each, these rooms are big for Paris, and good value to boot.

Hotel Montalembert
3 rue de Montalembert
75007 Paris
France

Tel: +33 1 45 49 68 68
Fax: +33 1 45 49 69 49
Email: welcome@montalembert.com
Web: www.montalembert.com

La Réserve, Ramatuelle

Côte d'Azur | France

La Réserve, Ramatuelle, is located just minutes from Saint Tropez on the Côte d'Azur and two kilometres from the beaches. Yet you're in a secure, private realm at one remove from the hustle and bustle. The property is set against the hills and consists of 11 classic Provençal-style villas with pools and private gardens. Each is different with interiors by top designers, the focus on space and openness allowing the Mediterranean sun to work its golden magic. All villas face the sea, and feature from four to six bedrooms. A housekeeper is at your disposal to prepare breakfast, manage your everyday requirements and look after your wellbeing. While the concierge is an outstanding resource for arranging leisure activities.

QUINTESSENTIALLY INSIDER

What makes the villas stand apart is the fact they come with hotel-level services, as per your requirements: a home chef, butler, babysitting, beauty and spa therapists and even personal trainers. Captain-driven boat hire can be arranged. Your skipper will show you what's what and who's who in this home of the superyacht, as well as some hidden coves for a picnic.

La Réserve, Ramatuelle
Chemin de la Quessine
83350 Ramatuelle
France

Tel: +33 4 94 79 14 28
Fax: +33 4 94 79 28 54
Email: info@lareserve-ramatuelle.com
Web: www.lareserveramatuelle.com

Schlössle Hotel

Estonia's beauty is well-known to those in the fashion trade (just take a look at the catwalks). The country's capital is equally attractive. The place to stay is Schlössle Hotel, Estonia's first five-star located at the heart of Tallinn's Medieval old town. The massive wooden beams, antique furnishings and green and plum décor give this unique address a luxurious baronial atmosphere. Each room is individually designed, with many guests re-booking the same suite time after time. The Stenhus restaurant is a must, with 13th-century vaulted ceilings and a huge roaring fireplace. Traditional breakfasts and imaginative meals, served with grace and flair, make this the best-rated restaurant in Tallinn. A Swedish sauna is available, as well as spa facilities, golf, sailing and bicycle rental.

QUINTESSENTIALLY INSIDER

Schlössle Hotel's unique medieval setting gives better-known cities like Prague a run for their money. Plus there are fewer crowds. An easy place to navigate on foot, it's perfect for a long weekend in snow or sun.

Schlössle Hotel
Pühavaimu 13/15
10123 Tallinn
Estonia

Tel: +372 699 7700
Fax: +372 699 7777
Email: schlossle@schlossle-hotels.com
Web: www.schlossle-hotels.com

Belvedere

At the Belvedere, you're five minutes walk from the Matoyianni, which is the main drag in Mykonos Town for chic boutiques, bars and restaurants. Yet within the resort's soporific confines, it's like being in a small Cycladic village. Built around a pool are 45 rooms and suites that nod to Chora's indigenous all-white architecture – you can see the eponymous port from the hotel's hilltop eyrie – set in richly-planted gardens of cypresses and wild laurels. These once belonged to the Mansion Stoupa, built in 1850. This house with its grand verandahs and sunset-facing views is where you'll find the restaurant (see the Q Insider). But the Belvedere is far more than the sum of these parts: it's quite simply effortlessly cool – the gold standard in small Med hotels.

QUINTESSENTIALLY INSIDER

The fact that Nobuyuki Matsuhisa decided to open a branch of Nobu at the Belvedere says it all. From June to September, this is the hottest restaurant on the island, serving the superchef's Japanese-Peruvian cuisine, from black cod with miso to new style sashimi.

Belvedere Hotel
School of Fine Arts District
84600
Mykonos
Greece

Tel: +30 22890 25122
Fax: +30 22890 25126
Email: contact@belvederehotel.com
Web: www.belvederehotel.com

Blue Palace RESORT & SPA

Crete | Greece

Don't be fooled by the apparent simplicity of the Cretan architecture. At Blue Palace Resort & Spa on the northeast coast, you've got some 142 palatial villas, bungalows and suites, all with private pools. Expect mind-blowing views of the Med, afforded by the cliffside location above the Gulf of Elounda (most vistas incorporate the Island of Spinalonga with its Medieval fortress). There's a world-class Thalasso Spa with 22 treatment rooms as well as three Thalasso pools, hammams, Jacuzzis, saunas and a gym. Eat what you like when you like, choosing from Mediterranean gourmet (L'Orangerie) to traditional Greek (Blue Door Taverna) to Asian Fusion (Asia Blue) to Italian and international for easy grills and salads. There's tennis, watersports and day-trips to the likes of Santorini.

QUINTESSENTIALLY INSIDER

Note the resort's Ultimate Guest Service. Use this to secure chopper bookings, a bespoke spa package, and if you're here on honeymoon, a boat trip and beach picnic replete with private chef.

Blue Palace Resort & Spa
P.O. Box 38
72053 Elounda
Crete
Greece
Tel: +30 28410 65500
Fax: +30 28410 89712
Email: reservations@bluepalace.gr
Web: www.bluepalace.gr

Elounda Gulf VILLAS & SUITES

Crete | Greece

Elounda Gulf Villas and Suites packs a big punch for a family-owned luxury boutique hotel of just 10 suites close to the main pool and 18, one- to four-bedroom villas, all with private pools and Jacuzzis. Some even boast their own gym room, sauna and steam bath. Yet its reputation is glittering (it has won Greece's Leading Villa Award). The right people come here (we're talking super A-types) knowing they can escape everything they need to for the perfect Greek summer sojourn (the resort is closed from November until March). Elounda is located on Crete, an hour's drive from Heraklion International Airport, smack on the sea. The Argo à la carte restaurant serves delectable Mediterranean and International cuisine, and there's a lounge bar, The Argonauts, for glamorous evening drinks. There's also a comprehensive spa with steam and sauna.

QUINTESSENTIALLY INSIDER

Every one of Elounda's vast accommodations has a view of the Gulf of Mirabello. You feel like you're on a private villa vacation – backed up by the five-star service of a deluxe hotel. A magic combination that needs to be booked early.

Elounda Gulf Villas & Suites
72053 Elounda
Crete
Greece
Tel: +30 28102 27721 / 0871 990 3010 (UK)
Fax: +30 28102 27811
Email: info@eloundavillas.com
Web: www.eloundavillas.com

Grecotel Cape Sounio

Attica | Greece

Grecotel Cape Sounio is more than the sum of its parts – 154 bungalows and villas with private pools and gardens, two secluded beaches, a private hotel launch, indoor and outdoor pools, and four restaurants serving everything from authentic Greek to Oriental. It's an experience, a resort with soul that's clearly been inspired by the Temple of Poseidon. Set on a 75-acre estate on the edge of Sounio National Park, this is a hotspot on the Attica Riviera that is within a 40-minute drive of Athens International Airport. How easy is that? This also means you can take advantage of Athens' buzzing nightlife. Not that you'd want to leave Grecotel Cape Sounio. Nor that famous view of the setting sun through Poseidon's Doric columns, visible in the distance.

QUINTESSENTIALLY INSIDER

The 007 Elixir Spa is ahead of its time in Greece, offering not only the regular gamut of massages, face and body treatments, but also Ayurveda, the fiercely fashionable South Indian form of holistic healthcare.

Grecotel Cape Sounio Tel: +30 22920 69700
Lavrion, Sounio Fax: +30 22920 69770
P.O. Box 112 Email: reserv_so@grecotel.gr
Attica Web: www.grecotel.gr
Greece

Kivotos

Okay, so Mykonos is all about partying. But there's another side – chic, glamorous and quintessentially Greek. That's Kivotos, a boutique 40-room hotel (all rooms and suites are different) sequestered on its own private beach in the Bay of Ornos, five minutes from the buzz of Mykonos Town. The restaurants are so good, they're destinations unto themselves – La Meduse for gourmet international cuisine, Le Pirate for Mediterranean staples. People-watch in the 'K' Cigar and Caviar Bar, or just chill by Del Mar, the swim-up bar. There's squash, a spa and two different pools. The look is white on cream on turquoise blue – pure modern Med – and the vibe feels relaxed, the sort of place you could spend weeks just soaking up the sun and the soporific pace.

QUINTESSENTIALLY INSIDER

Take a daytrip on Prince de Neufchatel, the hotel's privately-owned motor-sailor yacht. Do a spot of island hopping. It's bliss. One thing Kivotos has is great service, and on the boat, it's unadulterated.

Kivotos Tel: +30 22890 24094
Ornos Bay Fax: +30 22890 22844
84600 Email: kivotos@kivotosclubhotel.com
Mykonos Web: www.kivotosclubhotel.com
Greece

 *Vedema Resort*

We all love Vedema Resort because we all love Santorini, the chicest small volcanic isle in all the Mediterranean (sorry Pantelleria, but you haven't yet enough restaurants...). Open from April until October, you can pretty much guess Vedema's scene: high-octane summers in blazing sunshine at the one of the island's rare full-service, five-star resorts (you've got everything, including a chauffeur-serviced shuttle to Vedema's beach club). The resort is designed around a 15th-century winery. There are 45 villas with cupolas, marble bathrooms and terraces. Pool suites are divine, with views to the sea and vineyards. The spa is in minimalist 'Cycladic' style, handcrafted with black volcanic stones, and there's a Fitness Centre with sauna and steam bath. The restaurant 'Vinsanto' is among the most exclusive on the island and 'Canava' wine bar is a destination unto itself.

QUINTESSENTIALLY INSIDER

Book the three-bedroom Presidential Villa, possibly the best suite on the island with a private pool, open-air Jacuzzi and three bathrooms all with hydro-massage bathtubs. Yet the pared-back, clean-lined style ensures it feels relaxed, not vulgar.

Vedema Resort   Tel: +30 22860 81796
P.O. Box 539   Fax: +30 22860 81798
Megalohori   Email: info@vedema.gr
Santorini   Web: www.vedema.gr
Greece

The Westbury

If you know your Irish literature, you'll know Grafton Street, which throughout Dublin's history has stood at the centre of city life. The business district and Dublin's best shops are within a few minutes walk. For the culturally inclined, Trinity College is on the doorstep, and The Liffey and St Stephen's Green are both easy ambles. Hence The Westbury's status as one of the best located hotels in town. Facilities are top of their game – 205 bedrooms, two restaurants and bars, a gym, business centre and extensive conference and meeting facilities (seven dedicated boardrooms). But what makes The Westbury is the sheer charm of its service. And the Presidential Suite – ideal for entertaining as well as downtime, featuring a full entertainment system, sauna and gym.

QUINTESSENTIALLY INSIDER

The Westbury offers secure, free parking in the centre of town. So hire a car, and use it, for on Dublin's fringe lie some of Ireland's best restaurants (for seafood, head for Howth, a former fishing village a 20-minute drive from the hotel).

The Westbury   Tel: +353 1 679 1122
Grafton Street   Fax: +353 1 679 7078
Dublin 2   Email: westbury@jurysdoyle.com
Ireland   Web: www.jurysdoyle.com

"If an ass goes travelling he will not come home a horse."
Thomas Fuller

Cala di Volpe

If Sardinia is the playground of the super-chic, then Hotel Cala di Volpe is where the crème hang out – a serene, sun-drenched resort on the turquoise Costa Smeralda. Designed in 1963 by architect Jacques Couëlle, Cala di Volpe is perched like a village with porticoes, granite paving, a port and jetty stretching out into the bay. It feels authentic with two dining places that showcase, among other cuisines, the best of Sardinian and Mediterranean traditions (the Barbecue is famous worldwide for its seafood buffets). You will want for nothing: the largest seawater pool in Europe, waterskiing, boat rental, tennis, a modern fitness centre, beauty and massage salons. Resort shopping ranges from Escada to Brioni. Suffice to say Cala di Volpe is among the gems of Starwood's worldwide Luxury Collection.

QUINTESSENTIALLY INSIDER

The 230sq metre Presidential Suite is always in demand. It sleeps up to six and has a private pool on the terrace overlooking the bay. Add to this the signature Hotel Cala di Volpe service, and you can see why Sardinia remains in vogue with the world's most demanding privacy-hunters.

Hotel Cala di Volpe
07020 Porto Cervo (SS)
Sardinia
Italy

Tel: +39 0789 976 111
Fax: +39 0789 976 617
Email: res059caladivolpe@luxurycollection.com
Web: www.luxurycollection.com/caladivolpe

Castello di Velona

If you know the film, *The English Patient*, you'll be familiar with the Val D'Orcia – possibly the most beautiful swathe of rural Tuscany (which hasn't yet been ruined by the great British invasion). Castello di Velona ticks all the boxes. This 22-suite, two-room, 11th-century castle is better than a postcard, surrounded by vineyards, olive groves and slender cypresses less than half an hour's drive from Siena. The views from the hilltop where it's perched are extraordinary, and the outdoor pool makes for the perfect eyrie. When it comes to the kitchen, these are competitive climes. The Castello di Velona pulls it off, serving regional Italian. The fact they make their own olive oil and wine speaks volumes of an attention to detail, matched in the service.

QUINTESSENTIALLY INSIDER

For a wedding, birthday – for that matter, any kind of shindig – Castello di Velona is a gem, large enough to accommodate your core crew of friends. With a location this commanding, you can party all you like. The stars set the mood with a backdrop of castle, gardens and loggias.

Castello di Velona   Tel: +39 0577 800 101
53024 Montalcino   Fax: +39 0577 835 661
Siena   Email: info@castellodivelona.it
Italy   Web: www.castellodivelona.it

Hotel Cipriani

Venice | Italy

Isn't it just perfect that the most romantic city on earth has a hotel to match? The Hotel Cipriani is as synonymous with Venice as St. Mark's Square, which lies just across the water, all the rooms oozing classic Italian class. Further suites in the Palazzo Vendramin and the connecting Palazzetto Nani-Barbaro are linked to the Cipriani by a courtyard (you know you're in the right part of town, for just next door is Elton John's Venice home). Canaletto-like vistas include the Palladian church of San Giorgio. A resort of sorts in a city pinched for space, you've got a vast pool (great for people-watching), three restaurants, as well as a formidable new spa (like most things here, arguably the best in town). The penthouse has an open-air plunge pool, and for all guests, the hotel's private, velvet-upholstered launch will take you across the Giudecca Canal whenever so required.

QUINTESSENTIALLY INSIDER

Hotel Cipriani is all about service, service, service. For unadulterated love and attention, book the Palladio Suite in the main hotel or the Dogaressa suite in the Palazzo Vendramin. With so many private footmen, you soon feel like a modern-day doge.

Hotel Cipriani   Tel: +39 0415 207 744
Giudecca 10   Fax: +39 0415 207 745
30133 Venice   Email: info@hotelcipriani.it
Italy   Web: www.hotelcipriani.com

Hotel Pitrizza

Sardinia | Italy

With the refined sensibility of an ancestral island home, Hotel Pitrizza is among Sardinia's most discreet addresses. The hotel oozes the regional style (local marble, terracotta tiles) while updating it for modern travellers (designed in 1963 by architect Luigi Vietti, Pitrizza was completely restored in 1990). It consists of 55 rooms and suites scattered among rocks and flower-filled gardens overlooking the emerald waters of Liscia di Vacca Bay. You can be totally private or find glamour in the hotel's hub, the clubhouse, with a wellness and fitness centre, restaurant and piano bar. The rock-carved, saltwater pool is the hotel's other lure – chic and blissfully quiet with turquoise waters that seem to merge into the sea. On top of this, Hotel Pitrizza also has its own private beach.

QUINTESSENTIALLY INSIDER

A lunch or dinner on Hotel Pitrizza's terrace is a memory that will stick. It possesses a rare kind of magic, and that's before you've even tasted the octopus, melt-in-the-mouth pasta or the signature dish of Sa Fregola.

Hotel Pitrizza   Tel: +39 0789 930 111
07020 Porto Cervo   Fax: +39 0789 930 611
Sardinia   Email: res066pitrizza@luxurycollection.com
Italy   Web: www.luxurycollection.com/hotelpitrizza

Sardinia | Italy

Built by local artisans, the all-white Hotel Romazzino feels like it should be here – a refuge close to Sardinia's sparkling cobalt sea and sandy beaches. The rugged coastal landscape is decked in wildflowers and conceals romantic coves. Yet Hotel Romazzino is also modern, with all guest rooms recently renovated to provide palatial quarters featuring marble and mosaics. The views throughout are pretty staggering (if you want the suite with the money-no-object vista, then make it the Presidential). Gourmands should expect an embarrassment of riches: dine on the terrace at Romazzino Restaurant, focusing on creatively-interpreted regional specialities, opt for a relaxed barbecue, go light at the Beach Bar, or sip cocktails to the tinkling of ivories. There's a vast amount to do, from golf to watersports to spa treatments.

QUINTESSENTIALLY INSIDER

Hotel Romazzino remains one of Sardinia's best family-friendly hotels, with a Toy Club (for children up to 12) and popular kids' menus. Entrust your little treasures into the hands of experienced, loving Italian nannies.

Hotel Romazzino
07020 Porto Cervo
Sardinia
Italy
Tel: +39 0789 977 111
Fax: +39 0789 977 614
Email: res067romazzino@luxurycollection.com
Web: www.luxurycollection.com/romazzino

Rosa Alpina

Dolomites | Italy

The Dolomites are enjoying a moment right now – and not just Cortina. This is largely because of the Rosa Alpina, an exceptional 50-room hotel that proves how the love of a good owning family can beat the big brands. It's also a rare mountain offering, for the Rosa Alpina is as delectable in summer as it is winter (really). Located in the village of San Cassiano, it is home to the Dolomite Superski circuit with 1200km of slopes and 460 ski lifts. In summer, sports include worldclass mountain biking, exceptional hiking, with trails starting right at the hotel, rock climbing and horseriding. With simple, chalet-like exteriors, the hotel expands to the back and sides with mountain views and private gardens. There's a Daniela Steiner spa (the same brand at Badrutt's in St. Moritz – you get the picture), a stunning indoor pool, steam bath, sauna and jacuzzi.

QUINTESSENTIALLY INSIDER

Rosa Alpina's 10-table gourmet restaurant headed up by Norbert Niederkofler is ranked as one of the best in Italy. In addition, you've got two further Michelin-starred restaurants within a 10-minute drive.

Relais & Chateaux Hotel & Spa Rosa Alpina
Strada Micura de Rue 20
39030 San Cassiano in Badia
Dolomites
Italy
Tel: +39 0471 849 500
Fax: +39 0471 849 377
Email: info@rosalpina.it
Web: www.rosalpina.it

Masseria San Domenico RESORT, SPA-TALASSO, GOLF

Puglia | Italy

If you already know that the land of the trulli is desirable, you're on the money. The heel of Italy is on the up, especially now there's a worldclass spa. It's called Masseria San Domenico. At this glamorous Adriatic address, seawater treatments are the main focus (as every thin girl knows, thalassotherapy will have you looking 'just so'). It's pretty as a picture, a whitewashed 50-room hotel centred around a large, rock-encircled pool in 100 hectares of olive groves and orchards. Historical remnants include the original structure of the 15th-century masseria and a watchtower once used by the Knights of Malta. For those here to feast on fine Italian cooking and sleep beside the pool, no problem. But be tempted, at least by the Masseria's new 18-hole golf course. Alternatively, go explore those trulli houses.

QUINTESSENTIALLY INSIDER

Pre-book the 'Douche d'Evian' or 'Douche d'Affusion.' Both treatments are administered by two masseuses working with powerfully relaxing marine extract oils. Not that you have to throw money at the experience. The quality of therapist is so good that one pair of hands will usually suffice.

Masseria San Domenico Resort
Litoranea 379
Savelletri di Fasano (BR)
Italy

Tel: +39 0804 827 769
Fax: +39 0804 827 978
Email: info@masseriasandomenico.com
Website: www.masseriasandomenico.com

Grand Hotel A VILLA FELTRINELLI

Lake Garda | Italy

Bob Burns is an industry legend, the founder of Regent Hotels who went on to create one of the most unique hotels of our time: Grand Hotel a Villa Feltrinelli. This Lake Garda retreat is a diamond, small but perfectly cut. It's got history, the castellated, pink-striped villa built in 1892. It's got location, in a park of orange and cypress trees beside the water (it's also within a 2.5 hour drive of five international airports). It's got service (the Burns trademark) and decadent porcelain, cast-iron and marble bathrooms (another Burns signature) with spectacular suites. It has also its own boat. More than anything, Villa Feltrinelli has spirit, the kind that can't be reproduced by lesser clones.

QUINTESSENTIALLY INSIDER

Book one of the Premium Junior Suites in the main villa or Bob's Boat House. Villa Feltrinelli is open April to October, and of all Italy's northern lakes, Lake Garda right now is possibly the most fashionable.

Grand Hotel a Villa Feltrinelli
Via Rimembranze 38/40
25084 Gargnano
Italy

Tel: +39 0365 798 000
Fax: +39 0365 798 001
Email: booking@villafeltrinelli.com
Web: www.villafeltrinelli.com

Grand Palace Hotel

Grand Palace Hotel, like its sister in Tallinn (see page 20), is defined by her location. It stands at the very heart of historical Riga, a short walk from major monuments among the city's cobbled streets, in between the Presidential Palace and the Dom church. With just 56 rooms, the property is pure 'boutique' – a small hotel that puts a premium on fresh design, its light-filled interiors combining contemporary art with cosseting, boldly coloured fabrics, tapestries and antique ceramics. The rooms are dominated by blues and white, the effect a seductive combination of old Russia and modern Europe. Facilities include Seasons, one of the leading restaurants in the Baltics, and Bar Pils. The Orangerie serves breakfast and lunch. There is also a sauna, steam, massage suite, solarium and gym.

QUINTESSENTIALLY INSIDER

The Grand Palace Hotel is perfectly located in the heart of Riga's Old Town, in-between the Presidential Palace and the Dom Church, making it the ideal place to stay, not only for business, but also for leisure travellers.

Grand Palace Hotel
Pils iela 12
Riga
LV 1050
Latvia

Tel: +371 704 4000
Fax: +371 704 4001
Email: grandpalace@schlossle-hotels.com
Web: www.schlossle-hotels.com

Choupana Hills RESORT & SPA

Madeira | Portugal

Design buffs love Choupana because it delivers style with substance. Plus it's a good namedrop, for the architect-decorator, Didier Lefort, also did the super-chic Datai hotel in Malaysia. At Choupana, his partner was French architect Michel de Camaret. It's on Madeira, a whippet-quick 30-minute drive from the airport. The hillside position overlooks the bay of Funchal and the Atlantic Ocean (and my, what views…). What makes it so cool is the pared-back combo of wood, stone, clean lines and light – lots of it – while the detail, including Portuguese antiques, African and Asian design motifs are the sort you might find in the private apartment of a well-travelled friend. Plus, there are just 62 bungalow-style rooms and suites. Ergo: Choupana is small enough for you to feel like you belong to the design elite.

QUINTESSENTIALLY INSIDER

You've got a good-looking hotel here, of that there's no question. But to have a spa with this much integrity, well that's unexpected. Facilities include an indoor pool, yoga tuition, aromatherapy treatments, a hammam and sauna. You can also have rasul, an Arabian exfoliation that gives you the skin of a 20-year-old (well, almost).

Choupana Hills Resort & Spa
Travessa do Largo da Choupana
9060-348 Funchal
Madeira
Portugal

Tel: +351 291 206 020
Fax: +351 291 206 021
E-mail: info@choupanahills.com
Web: www.choupanahills.com

Abama

Recently opened, ABAMA redefined luxury on the island of Tenerife. Tucked away in Guía de Isora, it occupies a tranquil, lesser-known area on the island's west coast. The landscape is compelling (thankfully largely ignored by crowds who stick to southern Tenerife) featuring volcanic vistas and exuberant vegetation. ABAMA itself faces the Atlantic and the island of La Gomera. There are some 420 rooms and suites occupying a 160-hectare finca, or private estate. You will find little reason to leave the resort. There are 10 restaurants, your own secluded sandy beach and jetty, a Tennis Club with 11 courts and an 18-hole par 72 Dave Thomas-designed golf course. The new Wellness and Spa Centre will put the Canaries on the map, of that there is no question.

QUINTESSENTIALLY INSIDER

Don't be mean on your time here. ABAMA offers something for everyone, from honeymooners to children. Also, unless you're wickedly unlucky, it's safe year-round for sunshine.

ABAMA
Carretera TF-47 KM9
Guía de Isora 38687
Spain

Tel: +34 902 105 600
Fax: +34 922 126 100
Email: res@abamahotelresort.com
Web: www.abamahotelresort.com

Hotel Majestic

In Barcelona, the competition is steep. Yet Hotel Majestic retains enviable presence. It has a fabulous location on the Passeig de Gràcia surrounded by the modernist architecture of Antonio Gaudí. Las Ramblas, the Plaza de Cataluña and the Barrio Gótico (Gothic Quarter) are all within a short walk. The 303 rooms and suites secure her status (air-con, WiFi and interactive TV are standard) along with the Michelin-starred headline restaurant, Drolma, from chef Fermí Puig. Q loves the rooftop pool – a complete indulgence on a warm day. A coloured mural by Philip Stanton sets off the city views. A large number of celebrities from the artistic, political and cultural world have stayed here. No wonder. Hotel Majestic drips with Spanish glamour.

QUINTESSENTIALLY INSIDER

Take a note of the Penthouse. It consists of the 'Apartment Paseo de Gràcia' and the 'Suite Sagrada Familia.' Each has access to their own private terrace with views of the eponymous city icons.

Hotel Majestic
Passeig de Gracia 68
08007 Barcelona
Spain

Tel: +34 934 881 717
Fax: +34 934 881 880
Email: info@majestichotelgroup.com
Web: www.majestichotelgroup.com

Las Dunas BEACH HOTEL & SPA

Malaga | Spain

The location of Las Dunas Beach Hotel & Spa says almost all you need to know – between Marbella and Estepona, which between them, encapsulate the exclusive glamour of Southern Spain's costa. It therefore comes as no surprise that Las Dunas doesn't do regular rooms. Or hold back on service. Not a bit of it. Staff are among the best you will find anywhere in Spain, and all rooms are suites – some 88 of them – each with a Jacuzzi, a terrace or sun deck and view of the sparkling Med. El Lido, the fine-dining restaurant, is overseen by the awardwinning Juan Carlos Jimenez. And there are others, including Brasserie Felix for Asian-Med cuisine, and Las Palmeras, for a balmy garden lunch. An aside: Las Dunas is also increasingly popular with its state-of-the art convention centre (down here, the winters are warm).

QUINTESSENTIALLY INSIDER

Following the hotel's money-no-object refurbishment in 2006, Las Dunas now has a cutting-edge Serenity Spa. Use the Kids' Club ('Mini Dunas' for children aged four to 12) and escape, luxuriating in treatments using St. Barths products.

Las Dunas Beach Hotel & Spa
Urb. La Boladilla Baja-Ctra
De Cadiz, km 163.5
29689 Estepona
Malaga, Spain

Tel: +34 952 809 400
Fax: +34 952 794 825
Web: www.las-dunas.com

La Réserve Genève HOTEL & SPA

La Réserve Genève, Hotel and Spa is blissfully refreshing, a chic, contemporary-styled hotel to give the city's grand dames a genuine run for their money (better than that, you're only three miles from the international airport). Designed by star designer, Jacques Garcia, he wittily re-interprets the idea of an African reserve with interiors that include a tented restaurant, woven rattan walls and an elephant sculpture in the lobby with parrots nestling in lampshades. You have to know Garcia's work (Hotel Costes) to appreciate what makes the result more super-cool than kitsch. There are 102 rooms including 17 suites. Most have a terrace or balcony overlooking the hotel's gardens and Lake Geneva beyond. Le Loti serves French food. Le Tsé-Fung specialises in opulent Chinese cuisine with two private rooms recommended for intimate events.

QUINTESSENTIALLY INSIDER

La Réserve's all-white spa with a glorious pool is so comprehensive, you could come for the 'Quality Life' Program alone. This tackles age prevention, stress and weight in meaningful ways, making use of La Réserve's full gamut of specialists.

La Réserve Genève, Hotel and Spa
301, Route de Lausanne
1293 Bellevue
Geneva
Switzerland

Tel: +41 22 959 59 59
Fax: +41 22 959 59 60
Email: info@lareserve.ch
Web: www.lareserve.ch

Adam & Eve HOTEL

The Med-facing Adam & Eve Hotel in Turkey's Antalya likes to call itself 'the world's sexiest hotel.' To get a taste of it, check out the styling by Hillside Su's architect, Eren Talu. Rooms are postmodern works of art – from their soft white floors to their floor-to-ceiling plate glass mirrors. The bathroom's shower incorporates music, steam and massage features while the elliptical relaxation bath is situated in the centre of the bedroom. An immense 106cm plasma TV is mounted on the wall just in front of your bed. And all this just in the standard accommodation. Upgrade to one of the 24 Villas, and you get a private sauna thrown in along with a lawned garden and turquoise plunge pool. Resort facilities are positively comprehensive – a vast spa, six restaurants (from Turkish to Oriental), four bars and a nightclub.

QUINTESSENTIALLY INSIDER

Activities at Adam & Eve Hotel include parasailing, go-carting and even ballooning. The idea is that you won't have to rely on anything but the resort for the perfect postmodern vacation.

Adam & Eve Hotel   Tel: +90 242 715 2444
Ileribasi Iskele Mevkii   Fax: +90 242 715 2770
Serik, Antalya   Email: info@adamevehotels.com
Turkey   Web: www.adamevehotels.com

Hillside Su

Antalya | Turkey

When Hillside Su opened in 2003, it showed off the true potential of Antalya in southern Turkey. Located on the outskirts of this ancient city overlooking the Mediterranean, the resort is a temple to sensuous modernity replete with a to-die-for spa (and such good value: a 60-minute massage starts at €54). The all-white, 1960s-inspired interiors feature fibre-optics and mood lighting. This lends the place its cutting-edge spirit, while in the lobby, giant mirror balls and white day beds secure the vibe. Hillside Su is a hip, urban hotel for the lounge generation with a seemingly endless beach to arouse your Mediterranean passion. There are six restaurants serving foods from Turkish to Asian, Italian and the requisite keep-me-thin sushi. There are also three bars, buzzing with the bright and beautiful who have made Hillside Su their sunshine escape. For when northern Europe feels the chill, Antalya delivers a perfect tan.

QUINTESSENTIALLY INSIDER

Open year-round, this is a hip-as-hell spot for a small conference for like-minded brands. There are eight meeting rooms and a state-of-the-art business centre. WiFi internet is available throughout the hotel.

Hillside Su   Tel: +90 242 249 0700
Konyaaltı   Fax: +90 242 249 0707
Antalya   Fmail: su@hillisde.com.tr
Turkey   Web: www.hillsidesu.com

Çirağan Palace Kempinski

The Çirağan Palace Kempinski Istanbul is one of those historical addresses that doesn't have to try very hard to be at the top of the wish-list. It drips with spirit, for one half of the property was once the residence of the last Ottoman Sultan. It is also the only five-star hotel situated directly on the European shores of the Bosphorous. Thankfully, Kempinski Hotels and Resorts matches this rich legacy with exceptional service (the concierge desk will look after everything, from personal shoppers for the bustling souk to helicopter tours using the hotel's helipad) and state-of-the-art amenities. There are 284 rooms and 31 suites (the 11 Palace Suites are memorable) and an awardwinning restaurant, Laledan, serving both international dishes as well as Tugra-Classical Ottoman extravagances.

QUINTESSENTIALLY INSIDER

The Çirağan Palace Kempinski Istanbul has its own pier on the Bosphorous. Make the most of it, taking a private luxury motoryacht to some of the party palaces on the water (clubs and restaurants buzzing in summer) or for a lazy summer's lunch at one of the sleepy fishing villages.

Çirağan Palace Kempinski Istanbul
Çirağan Cad. No: 32 Besiktas
34349 Istanbul
Turkey

Tel: +90 212 326 4646
Fax: +90 212 259 6687
Email: reservations.ciraganpalace@kempinski.com
Web: www.ciraganpalace.com

dunhill

LONDON

London | United Kingdom

It's rare to find a traveller who doesn't love Claridge's. The grand dame of London hotels effortlessly combines old English class with modern style (just check out who's in that glorious lobby). Somehow her appeal endures despite a capricious London scene where fashions change daily. Perhaps it is the service – smooth, white-gloved, yet somehow un-snobbish. Or the Art Deco Bar that buzzes from lunch to late with familiar faces. The restaurant, of course, is the London home of Gordon Ramsay, the three-starred Michelin chef (a night at the Chef's Table is among the most exclusive experiences you can enjoy in London). The Fumoir, the velvet-bedecked cigar bar, is the champagne lifestyle perfected, and Claridge's afternoon tea an English institution. The top-floor spa specialises in Anne Semonin and La Prairie treatments.

QUINTESSENTIALLY INSIDER

Even though all 203 rooms and suites have been newly remodelled, Q holds a flame for two fabulous new apartments styled by David Linley. For peerless London views, consider the deeply glamorous Penthouse terrace suites on the seventh floor.

Claridge's
Brook Street
Mayfair
London
W1K 4HR
United Kingdom
Tel: +44 20 7629 8860
Fax +44 20 7499 2210
Email: info@claridges.co.uk
Web: www.claridges.co.uk

Hambleton Hall

Rutland | United Kingdom

Hambleton Hall is a stayer – a pedigree-rich, English country house hotel that has continuously held a Michelin star since 1982 and its Relais & Chateaux membership. This has much to do with the hands-on owners, Tim and Stefa Hart who dearly love this magical address on Rutland Water in England's rural heart. There are only 17 rooms, yet a staff of 65, so you can take this as a given: service is seamless. Room interiors are conspicuously unique featuring period antiques thus throwing off the formulas now endemic in chain-owned hotels. But it's the food by Aaron Patterson that makes for the truly sublime – seasonal (with exceptional game in winter) and rich in kitchen garden herbs, fruits and vegetables. The wine list is superlative, compiled by Tim Hart and his faithful sommelier, Dominique Baduel.

QUINTESSENTIALLY INSIDER

For a family, the Croquet Pavilion is a gem – a stone-built 'folly' located 40 metres from the main house featuring a master suite, second bedroom, a private sitting room with log fire and breakfast room.

Hambleton Hall   Tel: +44 1572 756 991
Hambleton   Fax: +44 1572 724 721
Rutland   Email: info@hambletonhall.com
LE15 8TH   Web: www.hambletonhall.com
United Kingdom

Le Manoir aux Quat'Saisons

Oxfordshire | United Kingdom

Le Manoir aux Quat'Saisons is one of those rare addresses you can return to and have a totally fresh experience. All 32 rooms and suites are uniquely different, from Lemongrass (just completed) to the über-sexy, red-bedecked Opium, to the split-level Dovecote with its romantic, 15th-century architecture. You also get a completely different gourmet extravaganza every time : Le Manoir is the country seat of super-chef Raymond Blanc. The restaurant currently holds two Michelin stars, and hell it's good, showcasing the power of understatement (the kitchens are largely supplied by Le Manoir's organic gardens, which form part of the property's 27 acres). Oozing quintessential rural charm from its honey-coloured gables, Le Manoir is only seven miles from Oxford and a 90-minute drive from Central London.

QUINTESSENTIALLY INSIDER

Raymond Blanc isn't one of those who simply adds his name to a five-star hotel. Le Manoir is his raison d'être (he also has a cooking school here). So when you see him knocking around the hotel, be sure to strike up a conversation.

Le Manoir aux Quat'Saisons
Church Ro ad
Great Milton
Oxfordshire, OX44 7PD
United Kingdom

Tel: +44 1844 278 881
Fax: +44 1844 278 847
Email: lemanoir@blanc.co.uk
Web: www.manoir.com

San Domenico House

London | United Kingdom

San Domenico House is a 16-room diamond now owned by the same people behind Masseria San Domenico in Italy's Puglia (see page 36). It's a three-minute walk from Sloane Square tube and within tottering distance of London's best retail fixes in Chelsea and Knightsbridge (yes, you can walk everywhere that matters in three-inch Jimmy Choos). The style is classic English – chintzy, comfy, with handpicked antiques, featuring panelling and Toile de Jouey in the much-loved Junior Suites. For business travellers, the in-room technology is all up to speed, and there's a rooftop terrace for a summer party of 10 people. Why it works is unique: for London, it's intimate, a townhouse hotel with the spirit of a private home.

QUINTESSENTIALLY INSIDER

What a perfect pied à terre for those coming into London who like to eat out (there's room service, a breakfast room, but no other restaurant on site). Be sure to book a Junior Suite – generously sized for London (even more so for the price).

San Domenico House   Tel: +44 20 7581 5757
29-31 Draycott Place   Fax: +44 20 7584 1348
London   Email: info@sandomenicohouse.com
SW3 2SH   Web: www.sandomenicohouse.com
United Kingdom

The Grove

The Grove is a new conversion of a 300-acre, Grade II-listed mansion that feels like it has been in place for years. Everything about this 227-room five-star works with the smooth efficiency of a hotel with experience. The crisp, sleek, 'groovy grand' interiors co-exist comfortably with the historical legacy and 21st-century technology. The location is both of the city and the country, located 30 minutes from Heathrow and 40 minutes from Central London. Yet it has views of the bucolic Hertfordshire countryside (a working canal meanders through the grounds). Facilities include an 18-hole championship golf course, multiple restaurants (including Colette's for gastronomic European), Anouska's Kids' Club, 23 function rooms for gatherings of between 10 and 500 people, and an outdoor heated pool, walled garden and tennis court.

QUINTESSENTIALLY INSIDER

Sequoia Spa is among the leading destination spas in England, with a full gamut of facilities that includes a 22 metre indoor pool and 13 treatment rooms focusing on ESPA therapies.

The Grove
Chandlers Cross
Hertfordshire
WD3 4TG
United Kingdom

Tel: +44 1923 807 807
Fax: +44 1923 221 008
Email: info@thegrove.co.uk
Web: www.thegrove.co.uk

Playtime. Anywhere. Anytime.

Africa & Indian Ocean

Abu Camp

For a wild African location, it doesn't get much better than Abu Camp in Botswana's game-rich Okavango Delta where the eponymous river meets the Kalahari Desert. But there's more to it than bush. Abu is all about elephant-backed safaris as pioneered by conservationist Randall Jay Moore. To view the region's great horizons from the loftiest perch imaginable is a rare privilege. You cruise for hours, led by the herd's much-loved matriarch, Cathy, to see giraffe, zebra, elephant, impala, wildebeest, buffalo and warthogs. Accommodation comprises unique Afro-Bedouin canvas-and-pole tents stuffed with antiques, opening out on to elevated decks sculpted around trees. And also – check this out – there's Little Abu, a new baby elephant belonging to the riding herd.

QUINTESSENTIALLY INSIDER

The Okavango Delta is the largest inland delta on earth, but instead of flowing into the sea, its annual flood (usually at its highest from August to October) spreads over thousands of miles of the Kalahari sand in a patchwork of lagoons. For those passionate about safari, this is when to visit.

Abu Camp
Elephant Back Safaris
P.O. Box 332
Maun
Botswana

Tel: +27 11 807 1800
Fax: +27 11 807 2110
Email: ebs@info.bw or enquiry@wilderness.co.za
Web: www.abucamp.com or www.wilderness-safaris.com

Alfajiri Villas

Alfajiri Villas consists of three houses on the East African coast. In Cliff and Garden Villas, there are four bedrooms; in Beach Villa, there are two rooms. You have exclusive use of your respective house, each with its own stretch pool, although the best option is to take the property over for a party (a 30th birthday here will be among the best shindigs ever). The whole place drips in kick-off-your-flip-flops-style glamour, combining ivory Danish floors, wooden beams, Lamu floors, Makuti roofs and eclectic African and Far Eastern artefacts. All of this in lawned gardens filled with palms on a pretty cliff above the beach with Indian Ocean views. Once paid up, rates include all meals (cooked to order), massages, golf and watersports. Two nannies are available 24 hours a day.

QUINTESSENTIALLY INSIDER

Golf in Kenya? You bet. There is an 18-hole course located just two minutes walk from Alfajiri Villas. Others in your party can capitalise on the on-call massage and reflexology service, available in beachfront gazebos.

Alfajiri Villas
P.O. Box 454
Ukunda
Kenya

Tel: +254 733 630 491 or +39 3485 100 972
Fax: +254 40 320 2218
Email: molinaro@africaonline.co.ke
Web: www.alfajirivillas.com

Amanjena

When Amanjena opened in Marrakech, it raised the game for this fashionable North African town. Travellers no longer had to contend with cramped riad-style accommodations in the Medina (the old town) but could stretch out and luxuriate in this 39-suite property on the city's fringe. Like Amanjiwo (see page 109), this one's built by Ed Tuttle and inspired by local palaces. The walls are a sun-baked pink and grounds feature vast bassins (ornamental irrigation pools), domed pavilions and regal rose gardens. Room details include zellij fountains (in the eight pavilion bassin suites), a pillared minzah (gazebo) and maillechort candle lanterns. The Thai restaurant attracts the city's knowing ex-pats, and the spa has traditional hammams. Amanjena's heart is the main pool, which is possibly the most glamorous in all North Africa.

QUINTESSENTIALLY INSIDER

The top suite is the Al-Hamra Maison with two bedrooms, a private butler and 40sq metre heated pool. Alternatively, Q holds a flame for the six, two-floor maisons – a notch down, but also two-bedroom, each with a courtyard and pool. The bathtubs are green marble.

Amanjena
Route de Ouarzazate (12 kms)
Marrakech
Morocco

Tel: +212 44 40 33 53
Fax: +212 44 40 34 77
Email: amanjena@amanresorts.com
Web: www.amanresorts.com

Jnane Tamsna

You need to know the provenance of Jnane Tamsna to understand why it stands out. It was created by Meryanne Loum-Martin, who after Talitha Getty, is the modern style queen of Marrakech. Despite comprehensive facilities, from five pools to a hammam and experienced massage therapists, Jnane Tamsna feels in spirit like a private house. This 24-bedroom property is located in the Palmeraie, the ancient date grove 15 minutes drive from the city's walls. An idyll of modern Moroccan living, the property combines glorious organic gardens with Moorish arches and grand salons, the rooms and suites each unique and eclectically decorated with Senegalese textiles and Asian silks. There are no strict menus. Chefs cook to order from the organic crops, combining French, Moroccan and Mediterranean cuisines.

QUINTESSENTIALLY INSIDER

With Berber rugs spread out around the pools with candles, caidal tents and musicians playing beneath the trees, the parties at Jnane Tamsna are famously unique. That's why Q rates it as among Morrocco's top five venues for a private event.

Jnane Tamsna   Tel: +212 24 32 94 23
Douar Abiad   Email: meryanne@jnanetamsna.com
La Palmeraie   Web: www.jnanetamsna.com
Marrakech
Morocco

Kasbah Tamadot

Kasbah Tamadot is unique in Morocco: a luxe retreat in the Atlas mountains replete with interior-designed suites, indoor and outdoor pools, a spa and hammam just 45 minutes from Marrakech. It's that easy, yet feels a million worlds away from the busy souks. The property is an historic building formerly belonging to the antiques dealer Luciano Tempo, and purchased by Sir Richard Branson who spotted the pink palace on a ballooning expedition. Tempo's eclectic furniture and artefacts were included in the deal. Now there are 18 rooms and suites dotted about the property, including a fabulous tower once used as a painter's studio. Staff are local Berbers, their culture reflected in the restaurant's menus, which also feature international cuisine.

QUINTESSENTIALLY INSIDER

The views of the Atlas – in winter dusted with snow, in spring with wildflowers – are peerless. It's a drama worth requesting when you make your reservation, that you want that vista featuring the long, deep valley.

Kasbah Tamadot
BP 67
042150 Asni par Marrakech
Morocco

Tel: + 44 20 8600 0430
Fax: + 44 20 8600 0431
Email: enquiries@limitededition.virgin.co.uk
Web: www.virgin.com/limitededition

Riad El Fenn

Marrekech has her manifold charms – Medieval alleys, bustling souks, as well as super-chic boutiques and maison d'hôtes. Riad El Fenn strikes the perfect balance. An early 19th-century mansion constructed around three courtyards with a large garden, it oozes the historical richness of the city's medina (the old walled town). Yet with contemporary artworks by Anthony Gormley and Bridget Riley, you've got something altogether more interesting, cool and fun. Unusually for this neck of the woods, there isn't just one pool, but two (the riad houses in Marrakech are generally too small for such indulgences). There are 18 bedrooms, all individually decorated, a library, spa with hammam, screening room, bar and restaurant (modern Mediterranean-inspired) as well as roof terraces, sundecks and hanging gardens.

QUINTESSENTIALLY INSIDER

Q's favourites are Suite 6 and Suite 19, each of which have their own private terrace. Each is different, combining leather floors with exotic inlays, a steam room and sunken bath. They also feature the owner's contemporary artworks.

Riad El Fenn
N2 Derb Moulay Abdallah Ben
Hezzian, Bab El Ksour
40000 Marrakech Medina
Morocco

Tel: +212 24 44 12 10/20
Fax: +212 24 44 12 11
Email: riadelfenn@menara.ma
Web: www.riadelfenn.com

Picture: Grumeti Reserves

"Like all great travellers, I have seen more than I remember, and remember more than I have seen."

Benjamin Disraeli

The Twelve Apostles HOTEL & SPA

Cape Town | South Africa

For a Cape Town vista, try The Twelve Apostles Hotel & Spa, backed by Table Mountain and on the edge of the Atlantic Ocean. You're also only 20 minutes from the bustling heart of the Victoria & Albert Waterfront. There are 55 rooms and 15 suites decorated in themes of 'Blue and White', 'Shell', 'African' and 'Natural'. Somehow, the hotel manages to strike that tricky balance between family-friendly (children of all ages are welcome, with children under 12 accommodated free of charge when sharing with two adults) and attractive to those on business (you've got ample desktop working space, WiFi and conference facilities for up to 90 people). Service is pure South African – naturally hospitable – and dining options include Azure, an awardwinning eatery for international cuisine spiced with local traditions.

QUINTESSENTIALLY INSIDER

The Sanctuary Spa is among Cape Town's best with numerous unique treatments. Make time for me-time, lazing in the sun – there are two outdoor heated pools – and adventure sports. Diving, kayaking, paragliding and mountain walks are all available nearby.

The Twelve Apostles Hotel and Spa
P.O. Box 32117
Camps Bay
Cape Town
South Africa

Tel: +27 21 437 9000
Fax: +27 21 437 9055
Email: bookta@rchmail.com
Web: www.12apostleshotel.com

66

Birkenhead House

Hermanus | South Africa

Don't even think about visiting Cape Town without venturing off to nearby Hermanus (a 90-minute drive) and staying at Birkenhead House. To understand her pedigree: Birkenhead is sister to Royal Malewane, among South Africa's most glamorous safari lodges. Hermanus is also one of the world's best land-based whalewatching regions. See Southern Right Whales from the infinity pool or from the privacy of your balcony. You've also got spectacular mountain trails, horseriding, fishing, scuba diving and winetasting tours all nearby. Plus an 11-room hotel that is so well conceived, appointed and tastefully decorated in a modern eclectic style (antiques, contemporary finishes, palatial marble bathrooms), you could still be happy if you never even ventured from this cliffside perch. The food proves Q's point entirely.

QUINTESSENTIALLY INSIDER

Q holds a flame for Room 5, which has a private pool. That said, take any suite with a sea-facing view. So book early for Birkenhead is small. Sleeping a maximum of 22, it's also a great place for an exclusive rental.

Birkenhead House
7th Avenue
Voelklip
Hermanus
South Africa

Tel: +27 15 793 0150
Fax: +27 15 793 2879
Email: reservations@theroyalportfolio.com
Web: www.birkenheadhouse.com

Cape Grace

In Cape Town, escape the hustle and bustle by retreating to Cape Town's Victoria & Alfred Waterfront. On one side you've got the activity of the working harbour; on the other, the international yacht marina. Behind lies Signal Hill and Table Mountain. Cape Grace is located on a private quay, a 122-room super-luxe address that is defined by quietly efficient service. All rooms have French doors that open up to the tranquil views. Detail is homely, from mini-delis in every room to cool, crisp sheets and bathrobes that make other hotels look mean. The spa features a sauna, steam room and mineral bath, and onewaterfront, the hotel's restaurant, serves awardwinning South African cuisine. Make time for a tipple at the Bascule Whisky Bar and Wine Cellar – a great place to sit back and enjoy the views. Perfection.

QUINTESSENTIALLY INSIDER

Cape Grace is unusually well placed for shopping, business, beach and boat trips. Make a friend of the Guest Liaison who will open up Cape Town, sending you off with a personalised Champagne picnic.

Cape Grace
P.O. Box 51387
Victoria & Alfred Waterfront
Cape Town 8002
South Africa

Tel: +27 21 410 7100
Fax: +27 21 418 0495
Email: reservations@capegrace.com
Web: www.capegrace.com

Ellerman House

Ellerman House is a boutique Cape Town address featuring nine ensuite rooms and two suites in the main house (see the Q Insider for the latest unveiling). It overlooks both the city and Atlantic (suites 7 and 11 have dramatic views). Styled as a home-away-from-home, you don't pay extra for mini-bar snacks (a nice touch that removes another hotel convention) while service is discreet, accurate and comes from the heart. There's a restaurant focusing on market-fresh produce (guests just need to say what they want and the chef will supply) while many choose to eat al fresco on Ellerman's terraces. The swimming pool is Ellerman's nub – that said, Clifton Beach is only a 15-minute walk down from the hotel – and the spa is simply sumptuous.

QUINTESSENTIALLY INSIDER

If you're after a private rental with hotel services attached, book The Ellerman Villa and Spa. This three-bedroomed home, with a further option of another two bedrooms in the spa, is serviced by a private butler.

Ellerman House
P.O. Box 515
Seapoint
Cape Town 8060
South Africa

Tel: +27 21 430 3200
Fax: +27 21 430 3215
Email: info@ellerman.co.za
Web: www.ellerman.co.za

Jaci's Safari AND TREE LODGES   N.W. Province | South Africa

This is easy safari – malaria-free, a short hop from Jo'Burg – and packed with game. The 'Big Five' roam the wilderness of 75,000 hectares in South Africa's Madikwe Reserve. Jaci's Safari Lodge has eight canvas and thatch suites with rock baths, plus the exclusive two-bedroom Nare Suite (note to self: must book for second honeymoon). Jaci's Tree Lodge, a short walk along the river, consists of eight stilted fiefdoms positioned four metres above ground in an ancient leadwood (a *Tatler* favourite, most probably seduced by those style-rich interiors). Both properties have pools and serve feasts of wood-fired cuisine. The bush barbecues are cinematic. There's no air-con, but the breeze is blissfully enervating. And the service? Suffice to say Jaci's is owner-run with assiduous, genuine care.

QUINTESSENTIALLY INSIDER

The well-trained rangers impart a passion for wildlife that's more than memorable, it's addictive. There are open-vehicle game drives or bush walks morning and evening. Children love it too, kept safe and inspired with specialised expeditions. There are hippos, elephants, wild dogs, even white and black rhino. Just don't let them hug a honey badger.

Jaci's Safari and Tree Lodges
Madikwe Reserve
North West Province
South Africa
Tel: +27 14 778 9900
Fax: +27 14 788 9901
Email: jaci@madikwe.com
Web: www.madikwe.com

Ulusaba PRIVATE GAME RESERVE

Hazyview | South Africa

Ulusaba, meaning 'Place of Little Fear', is one of Afica's best spots for buffalo, rhino, elephant, lion and leopard. It's located in the Sabi Sand Reserve, regarded as one of the top five in South Africa, bordering Kruger National Park. Owned by Sir Richard Branson, you can bet it's also a great place to unwind, a game lodge that feels more like a private home. Hence its popularity for celebrations. You can even get married at Ulusaba, which is frankly about as good as it gets. There are two lodges – Rock Lodge on the summit of a koppie sleeping 16 to 21 in eight rooms, set against the backdrop of the Drakensberg Mountains, and Safari Lodge sleeping 20 guests in 10 rooms built along the bands of the dry Mabrak riverbed (this one has swing-style bridges connecting treehouse rooms). There's a spa, tennis courts, swimming pools and wine cellar as fine as you'd find in Cape Town.

QUINTESSENTIALLY INSIDER

Don't be mean on time here and give yourself a week. There's so much to do, from twice daily game drives, to safari walks, to hanging out in your lodge while the wildlife roams across the lowveld. Take a helicopter, or retreat to the Aroma Boma Spa.

Ulusaba Private Game Reserve
P.O. Box 2220
Hazyview 1242
South Africa
Tel: + 44 20 8600 0430
Fax: + 44 20 8600 0431
Email: enquiries@limitededition.virgin.co.uk
Web: www.virgin.com/limitededition

Pezula RESORT HOTEL & SPA

Knysna | South Africa

Pezula Resort Hotel & Spa on South Africa's Garden Route at the Eastern Head of Knysna is just a 40-minute flight from Cape Town. You've got it all: rugged cliffs, sheltered beaches and Pezula's Championship Golf Course. Add to that 78 suites (four to a villa), an awardwinning spa and Geoffrey Murray's cooking, and it's easy to see why Pezula is an essential stop on anybody's Garden Route tour. Just make sure you give Pezula enough time. There's so much to do: fishing, canoeing, hiking, birding, nature trails, horseriding, tennis (and that's without employing the services of the Pezula jet and helicopter to take you further afield). Best of all, you get all this and a chic place to stay – suites, finished in stone and wood, which exude warmth and elegant African style.

QUINTESSENTIALLY INSIDER

Take either of the two ultra-luxe presidential suites, and you get your own butler.

Pezula Resort Hotel & Spa
P.O. Box 3327
Knysna 6570
South Africa

Tel: +27 44 302 3333
Fax: +27 44 302 3303
Email: reservations@pezula.com
Web: www.pezula.com

Royal Malewane

Royal Malewane is safari with style, owned and designed by Liz Biden, South Africa's answer to all things glam. Not only have you got the 'Big Five' in abundance, but expect a swanky 10 stars in terms of luxury accommodation. A hub of linked walkways runs between the six suites – each with its own wooden deck, rim-flow pool and thatched gazebo – and the Royal and Malewane Suites (both sleeping four). The central library, shop and dining area (South African ingredients in Mediterranean and fusion combinations) stand under the canopy of indigenous acacia trees. The spa has a reputation as one of the best bush retreats on the planet offering a range of African-themed treatments. Facilities include indoor and outdoor therapy areas, a gym, Vichy shower and a 25-metre heated lap pool. Not bad for the wilderness.

QUINTESSENTIALLY INSIDER

In any other part of the world, the accommodation would suffice for a top-flight vacation. Here, you can add in fabulous game drives and expert rangers including Wilson Masiya, the only working Master Tracker in South Africa.

Royal Malewane
P.O. Box 1542
Hoedspruit, 1380
South Africa

Tel: +27 15 793 0150
Fax: +27 15 793 2879
Email: reservations@theroyalportfolio.com
Web: www.royalmalewane.com

73

Grumeti Reserves

"In Africa, everywhere you looked was made for greatness." So said Karen Blixen, a point clearly understood by the owner of the newly opened Grumeti Reserves. Located in Tanzania's Serengeti, a maximum of 52 guests in three luxurious lodges and camps share over 350,000 acres with extraordinary wildlife. Sasakwa is the headline accommodation. Located on a rocky promontory, there are seven air-conditioned guest cottages all with heated plunge pools. Antique-bedecked interiors ooze the Golden Age of East African living: Wedgwood china, Stuart cut crystal, Lafitte vintage wines, seafood flown in daily. Except there is wireless internet and widescreen video. A Dermalogica Spa completes the modern detailing. Sabora Plains Tented Camp represents 1920s grand safari living, and Faru-Faru River Lodge, above the Grumeti River, promises exceptional wildlife viewing.

QUINTESSENTIALLY INSIDER

There are various ways to explore the wilderness: by jeep, foot, helicopter or horse. Note that Grumeti's Equestrian Centre is among the finest in the African bush, the steeds ideal for a uniquely exciting game drive.

Grumeti Reserves
Western Serengeti
P.O. Box 0
Arusha
Tanzania
Tel: +255 28 262 2074
Fax: +255 28 262 2075
Email: reservations@grumetireserves.com
Web: www.grumetireserves.com

One&Only MALDIVES AT REETHI RAH

North Malé Atoll | Maldives

One&Only Maldives at Reethi Rah confirms the brand's presence in the Indian Ocean. It's their second and newest resort in the islands, providing die-hard returnees with a totally different experience from One&Only Kanuhura (see page 77). Here, on this 109-acre island, space, privacy and luxury are paramount. Unlike most other resorts, you've not got one circle of sand but 12 sweeping beaches, and of the 130 villas, 37 have private pools (perfect for a honeymoon). Some have lava stone aqua beds. Others are over water. There's Tapasake for Japanese-style tapas; Reethi Restaurant for contemporary Asia Pacific and Mediterranean cuisine; and Fanditha, a chic Middle Eastern restaurant on the far point of the island. The spa is a destination in itself, offering everything from Tai Chi classes to the Bastien Gonzalez medical pedicure.

QUINTESSENTIALLY INSIDER

The Maldives' larger five-star resorts are generally located in the outlying atolls, meaning you need to travel by seaplane from Malé's international airport. Not One&Only Maldives at Reethi Rah. It's a mere 50-minute ride by luxury yacht, and the island is as spacious as you'll find in an archipelago pinched for landmass.

One&Only at Reethi Rah   Tel: +960 664 88 00
North Malé Atoll   Fax: +960 664 88 55
Maldives   Email: info@oneandonlyresorts.com.mv
                            Web: www.oneandonlyresorts.com

Soneva Fushi & SIX SENSES SPA

Baa Atoll | Maldives

In the Maldives, one resort looks much like another. Not at Soneva Fushi. The subtle touch of the owners is clear to see, she an interior designer, he an international hotelier and dedicated environmentalist. Located a 25-minute seaplane ride from the international airport at Malé, expect 100 acres of pristine, jungle-covered island with one of the archipelago's best lagoons (really). The flora and fauna give it spirit. The chic, pared-back 64 villas and suites are veritable empires, landscaped for total privacy with double day beds for lounging. Twenty-four have private pools. Cuisine is exceptional: Mediterranean and New Asian with some 700 wines, and there's an organic veg garden. Like everything at Soneva Fushi, the Six Senses Spa has rare integrity.

QUINTESSENTIALLY INSIDER

Sure, it's splitting hairs, but for blinding white sand book villas on the island's sunrise rather than sunset side. Villa Number 1 is a corker, located on the southern tip. Though a bike ride from the restaurant (no cars here), you feel like you're in your own private Eden. That said, don't get hung up on it: Soneva Fushi is paradise, whatever the room.

Soneva Fushi & Six Senses Spa
Kunfunadhoo Island
Baa Atoll
Maldives

Tel: + 960 660 0304
Fax: + 960 660 0374
Email: reservations-fushi@sonevaresorts.com
Web: www.sonevaresorts.com

Soneva Gili & SIX SENSES SPA

North Malé Atoll | Maldives

Water babies always fall for Soneva Gili, a private island resort made up of 45 vast bungalows that sit over the Maldives' cobalt waters (a bonus: it's a speedboat ride not a flight from the international airport). You probably don't want to come with young kids – the wife, yes, and the girlfriend, most definitely, but not the children, at least not until they're swimming. Besides, the interiors are so totally sexy, why would you want the occasion flawed? You can dine 'in villa' or have a table set up on the sand bank, eat in the Asian-Med restaurant, prop yourself up at the overwater bar, or go for a wood-fired pizza. Some learn to dive at the resort's PADI school. The glass-floored spa (yes, it's overwater) is downtime mastered.

QUINTESSENTIALLY INSIDER

You will either love them or hate them: the seven Crusoe Residences, each a freestanding villa in the lagoon only accessible by boat. No one can see what you're up to, and butlers bring meals. The water's gin clear, and the horizon, peerless. It doesn't get much better, as long as you like solitude.

Soneva Gili & Six Senses Spa
Lankanfushi Island
North Malé Atoll
Republic of Maldives

Tel: +960 664 0304
Fax: +960 664 0305
Email: reservations-gili@sonevaresorts.com
Website: www.sonevaresorts.com

Taj Exotica RESORT & SPA

Flic-en-Flac | Mauritius

Set in 27 acres with its own private beachfront, surrounded by both a still lagoon and the island's towering green mountains, the all-villa Taj Exotica Resort & Spa, Mauritius, delivers peace, privacy and a powerful sense of place (just check out those views across Tamarin Bay). The architecture combines Mauritian motifs with colonial influences. The resort's two restaurants serve Creole, Indian and Mediterranean cuisines. There is a substantial spa, a kids' zone, watersports, tennis courts and a fully-equipped gym. All 65 villas feature satellite TVs, music systems and digital videodisc players. So, yes, all the luxuries are in place. But there's also magic, of the kind that belongs to few beaches in very few places.

QUINTESSENTIALLY INSIDER

The butler service ensures that guest requirements are met quickly, efficiently and with a sense of personality (you will want to take him home). This is the Taj difference, on an island already well regarded for quality service.

Taj Exotica Resort & Spa, Mauritius
Wolmar
Flic-en-Flac
Mauritius

Tel: +230 403 1564
Fax: +230 403 1561
Email: exotica.mauritius@tajhotels.com
Web: www.tajhotels.com

North Island

North Island isn't just one of the world's most exclusive private island retreats. It's also a 'Noah's Ark', the perfect example of conservation meets high-end tourism. The accommodation – 11 breezy, well-spaced villas – displays a respect for context and style, combining driftwood with shells, rock and palm thatch. Yet there's nothing Flintstone about the finished look; the architects, also responsible for Tanzania's Ngorongoro Crater Lodge, are too fashion-forward to fall for that one. Cuisine is organic and locally sourced, reflecting the region's mixed heritage (from Southern Indian to African) with dishes dictated by guests. There's scubadiving, snorkelling, seakayaking, cycling, flyfishing and island hopping, and a stunningly dramatic ESPA spa, built into the rocks. The pièce de resistance (make that three) is the beach/es – white, powder-soft clichés of Eden.

QUINTESSENTIALLY INSIDER

Villas 10 and 11 are built into the incline of the island's principal East Beach. Book either, and you will get a bird's eye view of the sand, water and palms. Not that much goes on in these far-out waters. The point is the solitude.

North Island
P.O. Box 1176
Victoria
Mahe
Seychelles

T: + 248 293 100
F: + 248 293 150
E: info@north-island.com
W. www.north-island.com

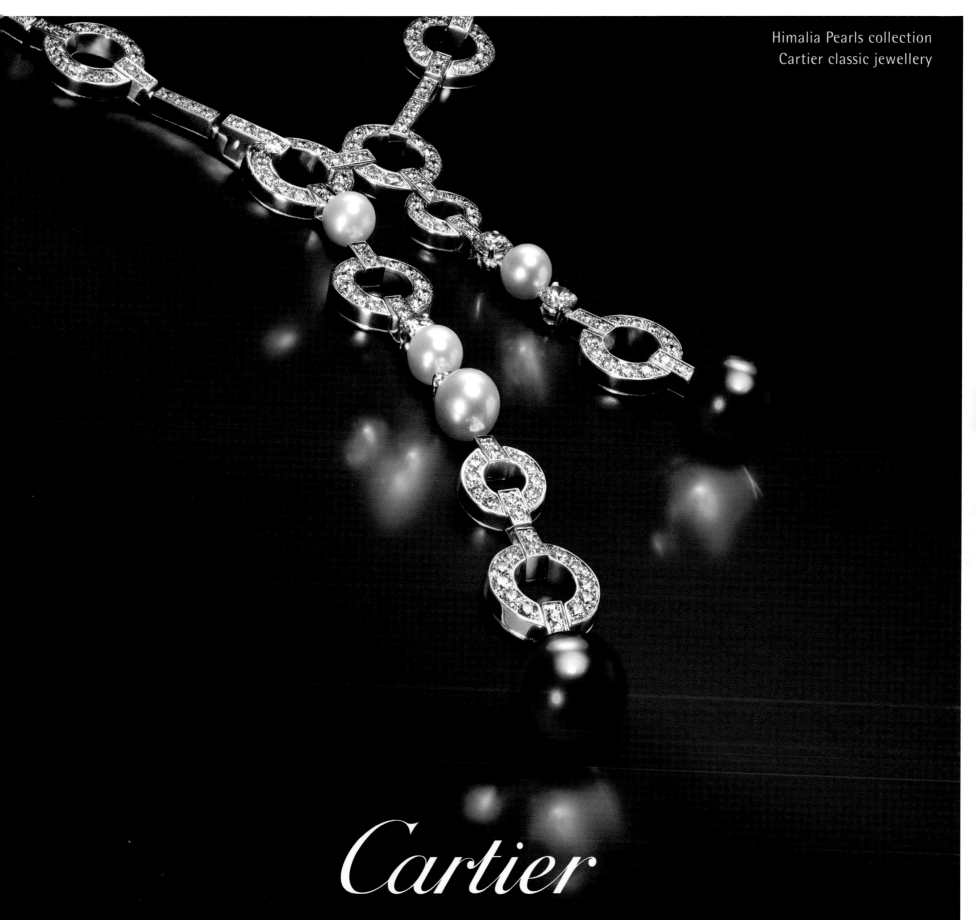

84

Middle East & Central Asia

The Emirates PALACE

Abu Dhabi | United Arab Emirates

Emirates Palace in Abu Dhabi, managed by Kempinski, Europe's oldest hotel group, is totally unique: 114 domes in mosaic glass and gold atop a glittering resort complex occupying a private mile-long beach where every grain is a perfect white. There are so many staff that even the beach is swept, while the 85 hectares of landscaped grounds are that well kept, you suspect there are yet more staff gardening by moonlight. All rooms have butlers. So yes, staying here makes you feel like royalty, from the miles of marble to the Swarovski crystal chandeliers. All 302 rooms and suites feature technology that makes other hotels look dated (check this out: the beach is WiFi). Conferencing facilities are the best in the Middle East (40 meeting rooms, a ballroom for up to 2,400 people, an auditorium for 1,100), and the restaurants, of which there are seven, make the Emirates Palace a destination unto itself. Period.

QUINTESSENTIALLY INSIDER

There are two pools, including a kid-friendly adventure pool with slides and waterfalls, and another, more tranquil zone. This sums up the Palace: whatever your purpose – honeymoon, business, winter sun en famille – the resort is uniquely large enough to cater to all.

Emirates Palace
West Corniche
P.O. Box 39999
Abu Dhabi
United Arab Emirates
Tel: +971 2 690 9000
Fax: +971 2 690 7879
Email: info.emiratespalace.kempinski.com
Web: www.emiratespalace.com

Burj Al Arab

Dubai | United Arab Emirates

Burj Al Arab is more than a super-luxe hotel; it's a landmark of the new Dubai and the world's most luxurious hotel. Fashioned after the billowing sail of an Arabian dhow, it soars up to 321 metres, occupying a man-made island 280 metres off Jumeirah Beach. All 202 suites are double-storey with floor-to-ceiling windows that command glittering Gulf views. All suites are bedecked in rich golds, with the headline accommodation displaying a panoply of colours (check out the Royal Suite, with its Versace-esque interiors scheme and revolving bed). Q loves the full-size Hermes bathroom amenities, and the brigade of butlers. The aquarium-like Al Mahara restaurant matches the standard set by its magical style with perfect seafood (there are five other restaurants, as well as Skyview Bar). The Assawan Spa & Health Club offers every conceivable luxury, including a signature four-handed massage.

QUINTESSENTIALLY INSIDER

Book the helicopter transfer service from the airport to avoid the city's traffic. Not only are the views of the coastline stupendous (you can see Dubai's manmade islands shaped like a palm), but the landing pad atop the Burj Al Arab is beyond awesome.

Burj Al Arab
P.O. Box 74147
Dubai
United Arab Emirates
Tel: +971 4 301 7777
Fax: +971 4 301 7000
Email: BAAinfo@jumeirah.com
Web: www.jumeirah.com

Madinat Jumeirah

Dubai | United Arab Emirates

Madinat Jumeirah is monumental with more than 45 restaurants and bars, a kilometre-long private beach, nine outdoor pools and an exceptional spa with 26 treatment rooms. Reminiscent of an ancient Arabian citadel, it features windtowers, palaces and opulent interiors. Nearly four kilometres of waterways meander through this resort, where guests are transported on water taxis. Accommodation includes larger-than-average rooms in Mina A' Salam ('harbour of peace'), which forms the gateway to Madinat Jumeirah. All have private balconies and Arabian Gulf views. Al Qasr is the 'palace' at the resort's heart, encapsulating classical Arabian heritage. At Dar Al Masyaf Summer Houses, guests can take one suite, a whole floor, or the entire 10-bedroom house. The Malakiya Villas are seven self-contained sanctuaries with individual courtyards, terraces and pools, each reminiscent of a palatial summer home.

QUINTESSENTIALLY INSIDER

Make time for Souk Madinat Jumeirah, a colourful and vibrant shopping experience. Meandering paths take you through a bazaar-like atmosphere. Open-fronted shops and intimate galleries spill onto the paved walkways.

Madinat Jumeirah – The Arabian Resort, Dubai
Al Sufouh Road
P.O. Box 75157
Dubai
United Arab Emirates
Tel: +971 4 366 8888
Fax: +971 4 366 7788
Email: MJinfo@jumeirah.com
Web: www.jumeirah.com

InterContinental Le Vendôme

Beirut | Lebanon

Beirut's charms are manifold, from her glamorous nightlife to her Mediterranean location to the fact you can ski and visit ancient monuments within a 90-minute drive. Not that InterContinental Le Vendôme is an address you'd want to leave, located Downtown facing the Mediterranean Sea. This one has got it all, including elegance (the design and architecture is reminiscent of a French private residence), gastronomic cuisine (Au Premier) and best hang-out (Sydney's Club and Bar remains among the hottest spots in the capital). All suites come with private butler service; for other room types, it is available on request for an additional fee. Not that you are short of service. This is a 73-room luxury boutique hotel managed by InterContinental so standards are high. The Business Centre is also über efficient, with IP Telephony throughout.

QUINTESSENTIALLY INSIDER

Make use of Le Vendôme's complimentary membership and transfers for access to private pools, a spa and Golf Club. This helps to explain why the hotel sustains a seductive mix, combining business and leisure with amenable rates.

InterContinental Le Vendôme
P.O. Box 13/5518
Ain El Mreysseh
Beirut
Lebanon

Tel: +961 1 369 280
Fax: +961 1 362 423
Email: reservations@levendomebeirut.com
Web: www.levendomebeirut.com

92

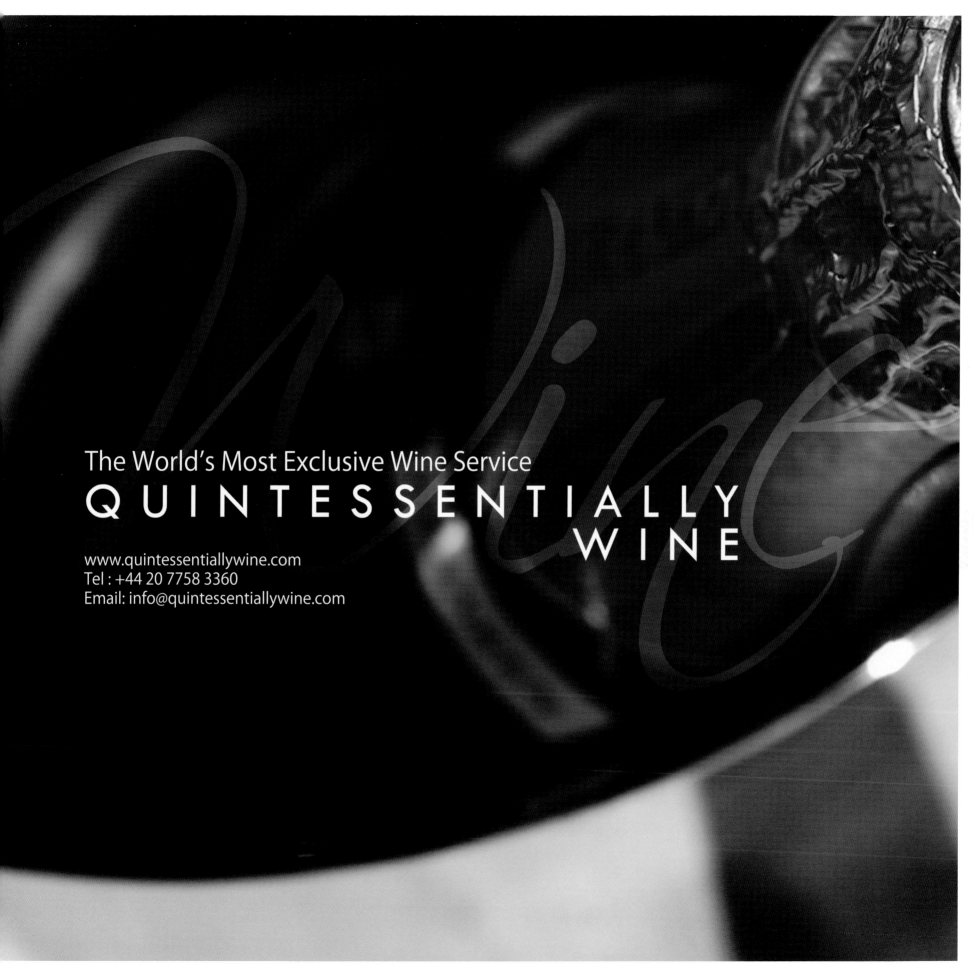

The World's Most Exclusive Wine Service

QUINTESSENTIALLY
WINE

www.quintessentiallywine.com
Tel : +44 20 7758 3360
Email: info@quintessentiallywine.com

"The use of travelling is to regulate imagination by reality, and instead of thinking how things may be, to see them as they are."

Samuel Johnson

 Thimpu | Bhutan

When Amankora opened in Bhutan in 2004, the world was watching. For the first time, high-end travellers could stay in style somewhere otherwise preserved from Western incursions (deliberately so, by Bhutan's Buddhist monarch). Amankora ('kora' means 'circular pilgrimage') consists of four lodges scattered through this Himalayan kingdom's central and western valleys. Amankora Paro is the 24-suite flagship. Amankora Punakha is an eight-suite retreat that includes a traditional farmhouse. The 16-suite Amankora Thimphu is in the Thimphu Valley (the capital's close by), and Amankora Gangtey is another eight-suite remote valley retreat. Guests travel between them – the backpacker lodge stepped up by 1000 per cent – although the Aman luxe factor is not the sole appeal. The landscape is exceptional, the culture alive, the combination providing rare solace for the most jaded of travellers.

QUINTESSENTIALLY INSIDER

Under Aman's care – the guides, drivers and spa therapists – guests can sink deep into the culture of Bhutan without compromising on comfort. This is the point, to travel in consistent luxury in a country otherwise rural and unchanged for centuries.

Amankora
P.O. Box 831
Thimpu
Bhutan
Tel: +975 2 331 333
Fax: +975 2 331 999
Email: amankora@amanresorts.com
Web: www.amanresorts.com

Alwar | India

At Amanbagh, you're in India's royal heartland, the architecture inspired by the Moghuls. Land once used for royal hunts now conceals the resort's 24 Haveli Suites and 16 Pool Pavilions providing welcome respite from the hustle and bustle of India's teeming towns (the pink city of Jaipur is a two-hour drive away). With domed cupolas and inner courtyards, pink marble and sun-blushed sandstone, everything about Amanbagh is sympathetic to the area's rich historical heritage. Even the spa treatments employ jasmine and rose oil once used to anoint the Rajmatas. The gardens are thick with palms, fruit trees and eucalyptus, and the restaurant serves both Indian and Western delicacies. Why would you come here? To imbibe the spirit of the region while enjoying pure tranquility. See it as a culture-rich break loaded with Aman luxuries.

QUINTESSENTIALLY INSIDER

In just one week you can cover the best of India, combining a four-day stay at Amanbagh with three nights at Aman-i-Khas (see page 98). The sister resort located a three-hour drive away is one of India's top spots for sighting tigers.

Amanbagh
Ajabgarh
Alwar
India
Tel: +91 1465 223 333
Fax: +91 1465 223 335
Email: amanbagh@amanresorts.com
Web: www.amanresorts.com

Aman-i-Khas

Aman-i-Khas is Amanresorts' second tented camp (the first is on Indonesia's Moyo Island). It is defined by its location, just outside Ranthambhore National Park in India's Rajasthan. Here, amid 10th-century ruins overtaken by jungle, you'll see rare Bengal tigers drinking from pools of water where crocodiles bask in the relentless Indian sun. The flash of orange is uniquely inspiring. Coupled with a stay at Amanbagh, Q would recommend it for the ultimate holiday, and the hard-to-get-right honeymoon. There are 10 luxe tents, all air-con with a dining table, armchairs, a king-size bed flanked by writing tables and capacious bathing area. On the terrace decking, find a canopied day bed and a 'step-well' for cooling off at the end of a safari. There is also a spa, Lounge and Dining Tents, the food organic Indian and Western.

QUINTESSENTIALLY INSIDER

Don't dawdle early morning, but be one of the first to enter Ranthambhore National Park when the gates open at 7am. Explore by 4WD accompanied by expert guides who will maximise your chances of seeing tigers.

Aman-i-Khas Tel: +91 7462 252 052
Ranthambhore Fax: +91 7462 252 178
Rajasthan Email: aman-i-khas@amanresorts.com
India Web: www.amanresorts.com

Taj Lake Palace

White marble, mosaic and seemingly afloat, the four-acre Taj Lake Palace sits in the middle of Lake Pichola in Rajasthan's royal town of Udaipur. Built in 1746, it is a folly of breathtaking beauty, conceived by Maharana Jagat Singh II against the backdrop of the Aravalli mountains and the city's lofty palaces. With Taj at the helm, the historical bequest is matched by watchful detail. All 83 rooms, including 17 suites, feature satellite TVs and WiFi access. The gardens are beautifully maintained. There's a bar (Amrit Sagar), a casual all-day dining restaurant with scalloped arches (Jharokha) and gourmet Indian cuisine available at Neel Kamal in the company of gilt and crystal. You can also eat alone on a marigold-bedecked royal barge in the middle of the lake. Just ask your Royal Butler.

QUINTESSENTIALLY INSIDER

The Royal Spa Suite is among India's best. Located in one of the palace's oldest quarters, this one-bedded fiefdom is set on two levels with views of the lake and Jagmandir Palace. Facilities include a massage room and private Jacuzzi.

Taj Lake Palace
P.O. Box No 5
Pichola Lake
Udaipur 313001
Rajasthan
India

Tel: +91 294 252 8800
Fax: +91 294 252 8700
Email: lakepalace.udaipur@tajhotels.com
Web: www.tajhotels.com

Amangalla

Opened in 2005, Amangalla made headlines. It recast the famous 19th-century Oriental Hotel set within the ramparts of Galle Fort on Sri Lanka's south coast. A UNESCO World Heritage Site, Galle is a 400-year-old bastion of colonial culture that brims with atmosphere. Thus inspired, the 29 suites feature period details – free-standing baths, planters' chairs, pettagama chests and teak floorboards (some 300 years old) as well as original antiques. There's a spa ('The Baths') offering hydrotherapy, among other treatments, and a grand restaurant for Sri Lankan and Western cuisines. Afternoon tea is a delight – as much a tradition here as it is at London's Ritz. The difference is the pace. Here, you can sup Sri Lanka's finest leaves in the perfect poolside kaftan.

QUINTESSENTIALLY INSIDER

We're splitting hairs – each suite at Amangalla is different from the next – but if you're on the island à deux, book the Garden House which is colonial-living on two floors with butler service.

Amangalla
Galle
Sri Lanka

Tel: +94 91 223 3388
Fax: +94 91 223 3355
Email: amansrilankares@amanresorts.com
Web : www.amanresorts.com

Tangalle | Sri Lanka

Amanwella is Amanresorts' second property on Sri Lanka (the other is located in Galle). Flanked by two rocky headlands, it occupies a coconut grove behind a smooth crescent of sand where the resort's Beach Club serves all-day light dining. The fact you can come here and see turtles lay their eggs speaks volumes for how quiet Tangalle still is (should you go exploring... Frankly, the temptation is to stay put). All 30 suites have a plunge pool and terrace. Two sides of each are floor-to-ceiling glass and latticed panels, thereby maximising grove and ocean views. You can see the influence of Geoffrey Bawa – considered the father of tropical architecture – with old Sri Lankan roof tiles and handhewn stone walls (nota bene: visit Lununganga, Bawa's former home with Italian-style gardens a three-and-a-half hour drive away).

QUINTESSENTIALLY INSIDER

Make time for three essential excursions: a visit to historic Mulgirigala rock temple, wildlife spotting in Bundala and Uda Walawe National Parks, and Lunanganga (not forgetting to pre-book a massage for your return).

Amanwella Tel: +94 47 224 1333
Tangalle Fax: +94 47 224 1334
Sri Lanka Email: amansrilankares@amanresorts.com
Web: www.amanresorts.com

Far East & Pacific

The Viceroy

Like a diamond, The Viceroy Bali is small but perfectly formed. Consisting of just 11 villas, it features its own private spa, The Lembah, as well as a fine dining restaurant, CasCades. The property is located on the slopes of the Petanu valley near the village of Nagi, five minutes from the artists' town of Ubud. All accommodation enjoys views of paddy fields, forest and balmy skies. Choose from Terrace Villas with dramatic 'bales' perched on the very tip of your private pool, to the two-bedroom Viceroy Villa that can be reconfigured as per the family mix (it's this flexibility, matched by service, that secures The Viceroy's reputation). Design is sympathetic to the Balinese context – stone, carved wood, tropical gardens – but pushed up a gear with lavish silks and state-of-the-art mod cons.

QUINTESSENTIALLY INSIDER

To arrive in style, book The Viceroy's Royal Service – private helicopter transfers from Denpasar, the international airport, to the property's on-site helipad. The journey takes a blissful 15 minutes.

The Viceroy Bali   Tel: +62 361 971 777
Jalan Lanyahan   Fax: +62 361 970 777
Br Nagi   Email: sales@theviceroybali.com
Ubud   Web: www.theviceroybali.com
Bali
Indonesia

Amankila

What makes Amankila stand apart from Bali's formidable competition is its pulse-quickening location on a dramatic cliff and beach overlooking the Lombok Strait on the island's east coast. All 34 freestanding suites make the most of this eyrie while the architecture speaks of Amankila's connection to the local heritage. The resort is in Karangasem, Bali's most traditional regency. So the suites, like palaces, reflect royal design motifs (you'll see the connection when you stop by Ujung, the water palace outside Amlapura). The showstopper is the resort's main pool – three 'infinity' tiers in rich green tiles (like the terraced paddies you see around Iseh) looking out towards Amuk Bay. There's a Beach Club at the base of the cliff, and another large pool in a coconut grove. The restaurant serves Indonesian and Western cuisines.

QUINTESSENTIALLY INSIDER

The pool suites are a must (there are nine, and be warned, they always sell first). Q's favourites include The Indrakila Suite, Kilasari Suite (this one with a pool), and the two-bedroom Amankila Suite with a spirit-lifting, sea-facing terrace.

Amankila   Tel: +65 363 41333
Manggis   Fax: +65 363 41555
Bali   Email: amankila@amanresorts.com
Indonesia   Web: www.amanresorts.com

Amanusa

Bali | Indonesia

Nusa Dua is an enclave on Bali's southern peninsula given over to the island's top hotels. With just 35 thatched and para-stone suites, Amanusa stands out from the pack – it's small, intimate and glamorous – located on a garden hillside with Indian Ocean views. You've got Nusa Dua's shops and restaurants on the doorstep, the international airport is just a 15-minute drive, and the beachside towns of Sanur, Kuta, Legian and Seminyak are all within easy reach. You're also next door to the well-regarded Bali Golf and Country Club. This is where Amanusa has its Beach Club, a great spot for barbecues, and one of Bali's best sand beaches. Eight suites have private pools. All have four-posters, sunken baths, outdoor showers and garden courtyards.

QUINTESSENTIALLY INSIDER

Amanusa is where the region's top executives come for high-profile meetings. The resort's conferencing facility accommodates up to 30 people. The adjacent golf course, spa and Amanusa's Beach Club ensure delegates decompress completely.

Amanusa   Tel: +62 361 772 333
Nusa Dua   Fax: +62 361 772 335
Bali   Email: amanusa@amanresorts.com
Indonesia   Web: www.amanresorts.com

Hotel & Villa Tugu

Bali | Indonesia

Hotel & Villa Tugu displays deep respect for the island's spirit, located on the pristine southwest beach of Canggu surrounded by paddy fields and Batu Bolong Temple. The aesthetic combines antiques and artworks as well as 100-year-old structures brought brick-by-brick and frame-by-frame to this ocean-facing location. There are 21 villas and suites housed in individual buildings concealed by lush tropical gardens. Each is different. The Rejang Suites have ocean views and feature silvered sunken baths created by local artisans, whereas the Dedari Suites feature open-air giant terrazzo baths and plunge pools. The Puri Le Mayeur Villa seems to float above its lotus pond (again this has a plunge pool and outdoor bath) and is dedicated to a Balinese love story of the 1940s. Meals are served whenever, wherever, venues ranging from a 300-year-old temple to a royal 19th-century dining room. There's also an awardwinning spa offering yoga and Pilates.

QUINTESSENTIALLY INSIDER

Walter Spies is the poet and artist who made Bali his home in the 1920s. The eponymous villa is exceptional, with a headboard made from the artist's original garden gate. There's a plunge pool, outdoor dining pavilion, sunken bath and garden.

Hotel & Villa Tugu
Jalan Pantai Batu Bolong
Canggu Beach
Bali
Indonesia

Tel: +62 361 731 701
Fax: +62 361 731 708
Email: bali@tuguhotels.com
Web: www.tuguhotels.com

Amandari

Bali | Indonesia

Ubud is Bali's artistic centre, flanked by rice paddies and the Ayung River. Every day, there's a temple gathering that sees the town awash with colour. Amandari seems to soak this spirit up, located on an escarpment above the jungle-covered gorge. The resort is designed after a traditional Balinese village with riverstone walkways, the main pool appearing to tip off the gorge's lip. A sacred path to a spring-fed pool revered by the Hindu Balinese lies at Amandari's heart. There are 30 thatched roof and paras-stone suites with garden courtyards, some with pools, others with views of the gorge or paddy fields. There's a spa featuring two open-air bales, a beauty room, sauna and marble steam. The restaurant (dramatic at night) serves both Western and Balinese cuisine.

QUINTESSENTIALLY INSIDER

For a private villa compound with five-star hotel services attached, book The Amandari Villa consisting of three detached, terrace-style bedrooms, a separate living room, garden, landscaped deck and a two-tiered pool.

Amandari	Tel: +62 361 975 333
Ubud	Fax: +62 361 975 335
Bali	Email: amandari@amanresorts.com
Indonesia	Web: www.amanresorts.com

Amanjiwo

Java | Indonesia

Amanjiwo, designed by Ed Tuttle, is clearly inspired by Central Java's centuries'-old temples. The best of them are on your doorstep. Amanjiwo (meaning 'peaceful soul') is set in a natural amphitheatre flanked by four volcanoes, the limestone Menoreh Hills and looks out onto Borobudur, the world's largest Buddhist sanctuary. There are 36 suites – from the size of the Amanjiwo complex, you'd think far more – with domed rooms and gardens rimmed with lilies. Each suite has a thatched-roof bale for outdoor lounging. Fifteen come with pools. Four-pillar beds, sunken outdoor tubs, brass gamelan gongs, batik pillows and sungkai wood screens conspire to make you feel like you're deep in Indonesia's cultural heartland. You are, albeit with a spa on site, with one of the island's best restaurants, tennis and nearby golf.

QUINTESSENTIALLY INSIDER

Amanjiwo provides the best possible guides to the mysteries of Borobudur. For privacy and cultural inspiration, enjoy a stay in the Dalem Jiwo Suite. This has two bedrooms, a butler and 15-metre pool set into the rice fields.

Amanjiwo	Tel: +62 293 788 833
Borobudur	Fax: +62 293 788 355
Magelang	Email: amanjiwo@amanresorts.com
Central Java	Web: www.amanresorts.com
Indonesia	

Hotel Tugu Malang

Hotel Tugu Malang is defined by the destination, in the heart of Malang's old city centre in East Java. It overlooks the city's main hall with a large pond of lotus blooms. This is Indonesia at its most romantic, the hotel decked in the owner's unique collection of antiques. All this in an elegant mansion featuring just 49 rooms and suites. Highlights include the Raden Saleh Suite, inspired by the eponymous artist of Java's royal family, with authentic island furniture from the 1850s. The Apsara Residence has a private spa, an antique canopy housing a large outdoor bath, a separate dining area as well as a sleeping suite with an antique 3.5metre-wide bed. There are various themed dining venues and three restaurants – the Silk Road Pavilion, l'Amour Fou, and Melati serving most authentic Indonesian cuisine, Spice Route cuisine, and Mediterranean fares – and Warong Shanghai 1920 for rare teas and exotic cocktails.

QUINTESSENTIALLY INSIDER

East Java presents a vast amount to do, from cooking classes to exploring antique stores, old Javanese houses, tea plantations and Mount Bromo National Park. Ask the hotel to arrange your bespoke itinerary.

Hotel Tugu Malang
P.O. Box 53
Malang
East Java
Indonesia

Tel: +62 341 363 891
Fax: +62 341 362 747
Email: malang@tuguhotels.com
Web: www.tuguhotels.com

Banyan Tree Bintan

Banyan Tree Bintan is about all about luxury and romance – 64 villas with unimpeded views of the South China Sea on the northwestern tip of Bintan Island. It's Indonesia, but if you're bad on geography, this is all you need to know: Bintan is 55 minutes by high-speed catamaran from Singapore. Perhaps that's why so many of the city elite use it at weekends (or for corporate retreats). The Pool Villas (some with two bedrooms) feature a private sundeck and swimming pool that overlooks the sea. Deluxe Villas, which are built on stilts, have open-air jet-pools on sundecks. Up here, you get a sense of the virgin rainforest at its most sublime. Explore further afield and discover Bintan's bays dotted with coconut trees, hills and mangroves. There's also a spa and 18-hole, Greg Norman-designed golf course.

QUINTESSENTIALLY INSIDER

It's almost worth coming out here for a meal alone. Saffron serves impeccable Thai cuisine and South East Asian specialities. Dinner on the Rocks (and to the sound of waves) is one of various private dinning options available with chef and waiter.

Banyan Tree Bintan
Site A4, Lagoi
Bintan Island
Indonesia

Tel: +62 770 693 100
Fax: +62 770 693 200
Email: bintan@banyantree.com
Web: www.banyantree.com

Amanwana

Moyo Island | Indonesia

Amanwana is Amanresorts' most remote Indonesian resort, located on the nature reserve of Moyo Island. You fly 55 minutes from Bali's Denpasar airport to Sumbawa, where you're picked up for a 60-minute private cruise to this pristine outpost topped with tropical jungle. Aficionados come for diving in waters considered among the world's most biologically diverse. Others come simply to hole up and hide in a wilderness camp that has all the hallmarks of Aman's addictive style. There are 20 tents located close to the water and beneath the canopy of the forest, each surrounded by coral-stone decks. They're air-conditioned with net-draped beds, large bathrooms and twin vanities. The Jungle Cove massage area sits under tamarind trees, and the restaurant is an open-air pavilion. Campfire dinners (Aman-style) are a must.

QUINTESSENTIALLY INSIDER

Charter Amanwana's cruiser, Ikan Gurami for some live-aboard diving in these exceptional seas. Non-divers will also have much to see – including 'Pink Beach' on Komodo, and visiting some of Indonesia's remote island peoples.

Amanwana
Moyo Island
West Sumbawa Regency
Indonesia
Tel: +62 371 22233
Fax: +62 371 22288
Email: amanwana@amanresorts.com
Web: www.amanresorts.com

Banyan Tree Ringha

Yunnan Province | China

Ringha is a way-out place, well known to Tibetans for it is a sacred stopping point for those on pilgrimage to Lhasa. A temple, minded by two monks, remains. It is located in the newly named Shangri-La County in China's Yunnan Province, a largely Tibetan region in the border country, with plains, snowtipped mountains and valleys (the trekking is fabulous). An earthly paradise of sorts, this is a land little spoilt with an extraordinary biodiversity. They say James Hilton, author of *Lost Horizon*, described the region when he invented the land of Shangri-La. You can see why, especially now Ringha has its first hit of a luxury hotel, Banyan Tree Ringha. Restored from the original Tibetan farmhouse, there are 32 lodges and suites, each with handcrafted wooden bathtubs and open fireplaces. Get this: there's also a Banyan Tree Spa.

QUINTESSENTIALLY INSIDER

It's not as hard as it seems to get here, especially if you combine it with a stay at Banyan Tree Ringha's sister hotel, Banyan Tree Lijiang (see page 116). The relaxing day's drive between the two properties incorporates one of China's greatest lures, Tiger Leaping Gorge.

Banyan Tree Ringha
Hong Po Village, Jian Tang Town
Shangri-La County
Diqing Tibetan Autonomous Prefecture
Yunnan Province 674400
China
Tel: +86 887 828 8822
Fax: +86 887 828 8911
Email: ringha@banyantree.com
Web: www.banyantree.com

 *Commune* by the Great Wall Kempinski

An hour's drive out of Beijing find Commune by the Great Wall Kempinski, among China's most unique resort projects. Originally the 11 four- to six-bedroom houses served as both a showcase for Asia's 12 leading architects (Shigeru Ban, among others) and a hotel. Now under Kempinski's management, it has been reinvented with a new Anantara Spa and another 21 villas housing 191 rooms (you can rent a whole house, or suite by suite). You're enviably close to The Great Wall, 10 minutes from the famous stretch at Badaling. Better still, you're a short walk by private trail to another untouched part of this extraordinary bastion. Nearby, there's horseriding and skiing (November to March). And, of course, hiking, the resort set in its own large park. Cuisine focuses on China's rich culinary traditions.

QUINTESSENTIALLY INSIDER

For a unique meeting or conference, facilities here are unsurpassable. The sky's the limit, with many delegations taking over all 32 villas. A newly-built function centre seats up to 500.

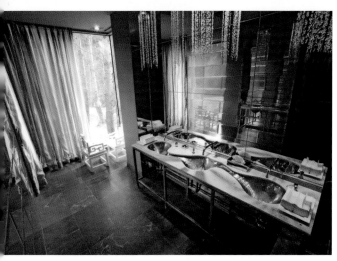

Commune by the Great Wall Kempinski
SOHO New Town, Tower B, 18/F
88 Jianguo Road
Chaoyang District
Beijing, 100022
China
Tel: +86 10 8118 1888
Fax: +86 10 8118 1866
Email: reservations.thegreatwall@kempinski.com
Web: www.kempinski-thegreatwall.com

Banyan Tree Lijiang

Yunnan Province | China

Lijiang is one of those quaint little Chinese towns that made it on to the list of UNESCO World Heritage Sites. It's easy to see why: cobbled streets burnished with the footfall of passing centuries, red lanterns casting pools of warm light, narrow canals, authentic restaurants and dusty antique stores. No wonder Banyan Tree got in on the act, the luxury hotel company recently opening a 55-villa property, Banyan Tree Lijiang, 15 minutes from Dayan (the old town). The architecture is inspired by the Naxi, the indigenous people, and each villa has views of Jade Dragon Snow Mountain. The aesthetic combines kiln-fired roof tiles, pink stone and grey Naxi bricks with russet gold and lacquer-accented interiors. There's a Chinese restaurant with an old-world elegance and a full-service spa.

QUINTESSENTIALLY INSIDER

While the region is good for outdoor activities (including trekking), be sure to make time for the awardwinning Banyan Tree Spa featuring a yoga pavilion and six heated treatment rooms.

Banyan Tree Lijiang
Yuerong Road
Shuhe, Gucheng District
Lijiang, Yunnan Province 674100
China

Tel: +86 888 533 1111
Fax: +86 888 553 2222
Email: lijiang@banyantree.com
Web: www.banyantree.com

The Landmark Mandarin Oriental

Hong Kong | China

Situated in Central, The Landmark Mandarin Oriental is made by its location (no wonder 'landmark' is in the title). The hotel has the largest average room size (540 square feet) of any in Hong Kong. Consisting of 113 rooms and suites, all accommodation, at whatever level, showcases avant garde objets d'art. Beds are enveloped in 400 threadcount linen and most rooms have not just one but three LCD televisions. Bathrooms are glass-walled with marble detailing. Restaurants include Amber on the seventh floor, while MO Bar designed by Adam Tihany (the Transylvanian-born American also responsible for the Mandarin Bar in London) is among the city's premier post-work hotspots. The 21,000sq ft Oriental Spa includes yoga and Pilates studios and 15 treatment rooms. There is also a VIP Sanctuary Suite (to die for).

QUINTESSENTIALLY INSIDER

The L900 Landmark Suite is spliced by a marble catwalk leading to the spectacular open plan bathroom. Clean lines, subtle colours and the best technology available make this three-room extravagance a Hong Kong must.

The Landmark Mandarin Oriental
15 Queen's Road Central
The Landmark
Central
Hong Kong
China

Tel: +852 2132 0188
Fax: +852 2132 0199
Email: lmhkg-reservations@mohg.com
Web: www.mandarinoriental.com/landmark

Amansara

Siem Reap | Cambodia

You'd visit Amansara because you want to see Angkor, Cambodia's famous temple-ruins. Or would you? This new Amanresort is a destination unto itself, a 24-suite retreat in Siem Reap combining terrazzo, stone and timber in muted, earthy tones. Each room includes a dining area, large soaking tub, separate shower and water garden. Pool suites have six- by five-metre pools. Some are grouped around the main pools (there are two, one curved in the central grass courtyard shaded by trees). Staff is the Aman standard (you junkies will know what to expect) and there's a spa, using Cambodian techniques and natural products. Food is organically grown and seasonal, and when the sun has fallen from its zenith, there's nothing like a late, lazy lunch on Amansara's Roof Terrace.

QUINTESSENTIALLY INSIDER

You're only 10 minutes drive from Angkor, the cradle of Khmer civilisation. Through Amansara, you can get the best guides (and take customised chopper tours of the region). To secure the cream of the crop, consult with Amansara ahead of arrival.

Amansara   Tel: +855 63 760 333
Road to Angkor   Fax: +855 63 760 335
Siem Reap   Email: amansara@amanresorts.com
Kingdom of Cambodia   Web: www.amanresorts.com

Pangkor Laut Estates

For indoor-outdoor tropical living, and a tour de force in traditional Malay architecture, then Pangkor Laut Estates in the Straits of Malacca gets it close to perfect. The eight residences, consisting of a private pool, garden, two to four bedrooms, living and dining pavilion, share the same private island as the eponymous resort. Except the Estates are concealed in Marina Bay, which is their own private cove, with clever elevations to maximise quiet and privacy. You can use all the resort facilities – the restaurants, the awardwinning spa, the watersports centre. Most of the time you'll simply retreat to your own private palace, replete with chef, manager and attendants. As Luciano Pavarotti said, "I almost cried to see how beautiful God had made this paradise."

QUINTESSENTIALLY INSIDER

Pangkor Laut Estates is set in a two million-year-old jungle on a 300-acre private island. No stay is therefore complete without exploring further into the forest's depths, in the careful, knowledgeable hands of Uncle Yip, the islands's resident naturalist.

Pangkor Laut Estates
Pangkor Laut Island
32200
Lumut
Perak
Malaysia

Tel: +60 5699 1100
Fax: +60 5699 1200
Email: estates@ytlhotels.com.my
Web: www.pangkorlautestates.com

Amanpulo

Cognoscenti come to the Philippines for some of the world's best diving, sailing and deep-sea game fishing. Super-cognoscenti come to Amanpulo, Amanresorts' island in the Quiniluban group of Cuyo Islands. If you want privacy, no-one will know where the hell you've got to. There are some seven square kilometres of reef just 300 metres offshore. Aquaventure, Amanpulo's dive company, offers courses from introductory to advanced. There's the full gamut of watersports available, spa treatments and tennis. And the Aman trademark – 40 separate casitas, each larger than most Manhattan apartments – as well as perfected service. Getting here is part of the magic. From Manila, Amanpulo arranges a private plane to Pamalican Island, a one-hour flight over some of the world's most dramatic seascapes featuring tropical green, brilliant turquoise and dazzling curls of white.

QUINTESSENTIALLY INSIDER

Amanpulo is situated just outside the typhoon belt so you can pretty much take your pick which month to visit. It's dry from November to May, with scattered showers June to October (when the island's tropical foliage takes on growth). We vote for December, for a leisurely winter holiday in balmy sun.

Amanpulo
Pamalican Island
P.O. Box 456
Pasay Tramo Post Office
Pasay City 1300
Philippines
Tel: +63 2 759 4040
Fax: +63 2 759 4044
Email: amanpulo@amanresorts.com
Web: www.amanresorts.com

JAGUAR

XK/R

"Though we travel the world over to find the beautiful, we must carry it with us or we find it not."

Ralph Waldo Emerson

Amanpuri

Amanpuri not only put Phuket on the map; it was the boutique resort that secured the Amanresorts name in Asia, creating a dedicated following who have never looked back. Why so? Each of the 40 pavilions is a palace unto itself, located on a dramatic bluff covered with coconut palms. Some 30 private villas (multiple bedrooms, private pools, personal staff) are located on the other side of the plantation. The pool – and this is a feature of most of the group's hotels – makes your heart race, a swatch of green-black tiles flanked by two restaurants. Below lies the beach on a creamy crescent of sand. Aman always gets its locations just right, and here, you can see why. Amanpuri has the largest resort-based fleet of cruisers and sailing vessels in South East Asia. Explore the region's limestone outcrops to discover your own private coves and pearly-white beaches.

QUINTESSENTIALLY INSIDER

At Amanpuri, you pay for the view. Pavilions 103 and 105 command the best vistas of the Andaman Sea. That said, if you take one of the 25 Superior Garden Pavilions, you won't be short-changed. Concealed by palms, they are totally private.

Amanpuri
Pansea Beach
Phuket 83000
Thailand

Tel: +66 76 324 333
Fax: +66 76 324 100
Email: amanpuri@amanresorts.com
Web: www.amanresorts.com

Sila Evason Hideaway & SPA AT SAMUI

Koh Samui | Thailand

Koh Samui is dear to many a traveller's heart. This is a place where fun-seekers once got up to all manner of mischief during the Thai island's first flush of fashion in the late 1980s. Now Koh Samui has thrown off the mantle of cheap beachside shacks and delivered a properly grown-up resort: Sila Evason Hideaway & Spa at Samui. Of the 66 villas, 52 have private infinity-edged pools. They are all split-level, soaked with light. The resort is set in 20 acres of soul-stirring headland, with views out to the Gulf of Siam and outlying islands (remember *The Beach?* It's that kind of vista). Dining is easy-come, easy-go, with different bars and restaurants. Cuisine ranges from Asian-Fusion to Thai to Mediterranean.

QUINTESSENTIALLY INSIDER

The double spa treatment rooms, both indoor and outdoor, are just the thing if you're on Samui à deux. And the treatments? Enough said (you can probably tell from the sister properties in this book how much Six Senses spas mean to the world-weary). The pool butlers are also a bonus.

Sila Evason Hideaway & Spa at Samui
9/10 Moo 5 Baan Plai Laem
Bophut, Koh Samui
Suratthani 84320
Thailand

Tel: +66 77 245 678
Fax: +66 77 245 671
Email: reservations-samui@evasonhideaways.com
Web: www.evasonhideaways.com

Evason Hideaway & SIX SENSES SPA AT HUA HIN   Thailand

Staying at the Evason Hideaway & Six Senses Spa at Hua Hin is a bit like taking your own private house in Thailand but getting five-star hotel service attached. There's no poor man's room squirreled at the back without a view. Absolutely not. Even the most modest villas have their own private pool... and terrace, garden and outdoor bathtub. You even get a personal butler who will cook up a barbecue. This level of privacy distinguishes the hotel from others in Hua Hin – resorts tend to be large on this popular coastal stretch – which is an easy three-hour drive or 30-minute flight south from Bangkok. The Earth Spa by Six Senses is up there with Asia's best, pairing its treatments with fresh, organic cuisine available at two restaurants.

QUINTESSENTIALLY INSIDER

Many of the ingredients used in the spa treatments are grown at the Evason Hideaway, including rice, coconut, avocado, papaya, aloe vera, cucumber, lemongrass, ginger and turmeric. Make the most of all those antioxidants – and book a daily treatment.

Evason Hideaway & Six Senses Spa at Hua Hin
9/22 Moo 3 Paknampran
Pranburi
Prachuap Khiri Khan 77220
Thailand
Tel: +66 32 618 200
Fax: +66 32 618 201
Email: reservations-huahin@evasonhideaways.com
Web: www.sixsenses.com

Banyan Tree Phuket

Phuket | Thailand

Banyan Tree Phuket is one of those places where you'll literally want for nothing. This full-service resort is built to satisfy every passion, from spa to golf. The resort occupies Bang Tao Bay on Phuket's northwest coast. It's part of Laguna Phuket, an integrated resort development that consists of five luxury hotels, six lagoons, 600 acres of parkland, three kilometres of beach and a vast array of dining and recreational facilities. At Banyan Tree Phuket alone, there are 149 villas, including Spa Pool Villas for treatments 'at home'. Most are one-bedroom and all come with king-size beds. Bring the restaurant to you (a popular honeymooner's habit) and dine on any of Banyan Tree's cuisines – exotic Asian to international to healthy – enjoying the romanticism of a villa you can call your own.

QUINTESSENTIALLY INSIDER

Be one of the first to book the new Double Pool Villas. These compounds are distinguished by 10-metre private pools that stretch into the lagoon. Step from bed to water and enjoy uninterrupted views, waited on 24 hours by private butlers.

Banyan Tree Phuket
33, 33/27 Moo 4 Srisoonthorn Road
Cherngtalay
Ampur Talang
Phuket 83110
Thailand
Tel: +66 76 324 374
Fax: +66 76 324 375
Email: phuket@banyantree.com
Web: www.banyantree.com

Evason Hideaway & SIX SENSES SPA AT ANA MANDARA

Khanh Hoa Province | Vietnam

This one wins all the prizes, and it's easy to see why: a contemporary boutique resort that properly reflects its location on the Vietnam coast without falling foul of either aesthetic. You feel like Evason Hideaway & Six Senses Spa at Ana Mandara should be here, tucked among rock formations, coral reefs and white sandy beaches with towering mountains behind, in Ninh Van Bay. Immerse yourself in the local culture, with river, mountain and cultural trips, or hole up at the Six Senses Spa. There are rock villas, beach villas, water villas, hilltop villas, spa suite villas and a Presidential suite – 54 different palaces for every mood/every friend. And the cuisine, East meets West, will excite for a full two weeks, which isn't easy at a place so blissfully cut-off.

QUINTESSENTIALLY INSIDER

Book up spa time before you arrive. You can add more treatments once you're in Vietnam, but the team is so good, best to get a daily massage in the bag. Then there's the diving, island hopping and doing nothing but laze in the sun, looking out to sea while the 'Blackberry Thumb' heals.

Evason Hideaway & Six Senses Spa
at Ana Mandara
Ninh Hoa Town
Khanh Hoa Province
Vietnam

Tel: +84 58 728 222
Fax: +84 58 728 223
Email: reservations-vietnam@evasonhideaways.com
Web: www.sixsenses.com

Palazzo Versace

The Gold Coast in Southern Queensland is Australia's El Dorado, and home to a logo-tastic hotel devoted to total luxury and glamour. Palazzo Versace, a 54-suite waterfront resort glitters with marble, mosaics and jewel-like colours à la the Italian fashion empire. Though room rates aren't crippling, it seems to drip with opulence, with Versace products everywhere (the boutique has to be the best hotel shop anywhere), a 90-berth marina, three restaurants (the wine list is extraordinary) and super-plush spa with double treatment rooms. You're only 100 metres from the surf beach, and a 70-minute drive from Brisbane International Airport. So, if you're a Versace type – and you know who you are – then this is heaven. For honeymooners, it's more than memorable, the service as loving as the branding is conspicuous.

QUINTESSENTIALLY INSIDER

For an Elton moment, book one of the Lagoon Rooms with a two-person Jacuzzi spa and a glittering view of the resort's lagoon pool. Throughout, you've got Versace homewares and Versace-designed amenities.

Palazzo Versace
Sea World Drive
P.O. Box 137
Main Beach
Queensland 4217
Australia

Tel: +61 7 5509 8000
Fax: +61 7 5509 8888
Email: reservations@palazzoversace.com
Web: www.palazzoversace.com

St. Regis RESORT, BORA BORA

Bora Bora | French Polynesia

Opened in June 2006, St. Regis Resort, Bora Bora has raised the bar in French Polynesia. Edged by powdery sands and a tranquil lagoon, this resort represents the epitome of carefree elegance. 100 exquisitely designed air-conditioned guest rooms are highlighted by overwater and beach villas, many with terrace whirlpools or private swimming pools. The one-, two- and three-bedroom villas range in size from 1,550 square feet to the resort's ultra-luxurious 13,000sq ft Royal Estate. Three delectable restaurants await you, including an overwater dining room, namely 'Lagoon', featuring Mediterranean and Pacific Fusion cuisine masterminded by New York celebrity chef, Jean-Georges Vongerichten. For dreamy relaxation, there's a main pool with swim-up bar and a romantic adult pool with private day beds. Spa Miri Miri at St. Regis Resort, Bora Bora , on its own private lagoon island, offers a state-of-the-art fitness centre and an incomparable array of island-inspired indulgences.

QUINTESSENTIALLY INSIDER

With the opening of St. Regis Resort, Bora Bora you'll need to think hard between the South Pacific and the Maldives. The Royal Estate or the equally elegant and spacious beach villas almost decide it. This is the overwater villa perfected with views not just of the South Pacific but of Bora Bora's emerald Mount Otemanu – carefree elegance in an exclusive setting.

St. Regis Resort, Bora Bora
Motu Ome'e – BP506
Bora Bora
French Polynesia 98730

Tel: +11 689 607 888
Fax: +11 689 607 856
Email: reservations@stregisborabora.com
Web: www.stregis.com/borabora

Royal Davui

Lami | Fiji

You reach Royal Davui by helicopter, a 40-minute flight from Fiji's international airport. A private, eight-acre island, you can only imagine how pristine the white sand, rich the coral reefs and clear the blue waters that bristle with fish and sometimes turtles. Thank God the owners chose to build only 16 villas, thereby protecting the serenity of this precious location. The Vales (Fijian for Home) are well spaced, each featuring two pavilions, for living and sleeping, joined by a covered walkway. All villas have a private plunge pool. Naturally, cuisine focuses on fresh local seafood combined with Pacific Rim motifs. The diving is impressive (the Beqa Lagoon is justifiably famous) with a wide variety of sites within 20 minutes of the resort. Alternatively, stick to snorkelling or retreat to the spa.

QUINTESSENTIALLY INSIDER

Book the Davui Suite with handcarved double doors opening onto an indoor garden. The plunge pool is gloriously spacious, and the views a soul-rocking 270 degrees.

Royal Davui Island Resort, Fiji
P.O. Box 3171
Lami
Fiji Islands

Tel: +679 3361 624
Fax: +679 3361 253
Email: res@royaldavui.com
Web: www.royaldavui.com

North & Latin America

Hotel Godin MONTREAL

Montreal | Canada

Built in 1914 as the very first poured concrete structure in North America, the Hotel Godin is historical and hip – a unique combination that wends its way into interiors, some ceilings and walls simply sheets of unfinished concrete. Find it in the Theater district amid the city's best shops and restaurants, near Chinatown and the Old Port of Montreal. There are 136 guestrooms including 13 suites, each with 27-inch LCD TVs, two telephone lines, wired Internet access and Egyptian cotton sheets. The hotel's Executive Suites offer an adjacent studio (great for private meetings). A new restaurant comes on line in 2007, and spa treatments can be arranged upon request. Aside from the aesthetic, what makes Hotel Godin stand apart is its personable style, putting it a notch above the institutional approach of other deluxe hotels.

QUINTESSENTIALLY INSIDER

Hotel Godin's presidential suite located on the top floor of the property features contemporary décor and dramatic floor-to-ceiling windows. You feel like you're sleeping among the clouds.

Hotel Godin Montreal
10 Sherbrooke West
Montreal
Quebec H2X 4C9
Canada

Tel: +1 514 843 6000
Fax: +1 514 843 6810
Email: reservations@hotelgodin.com
Web: www.hotelgodin.com

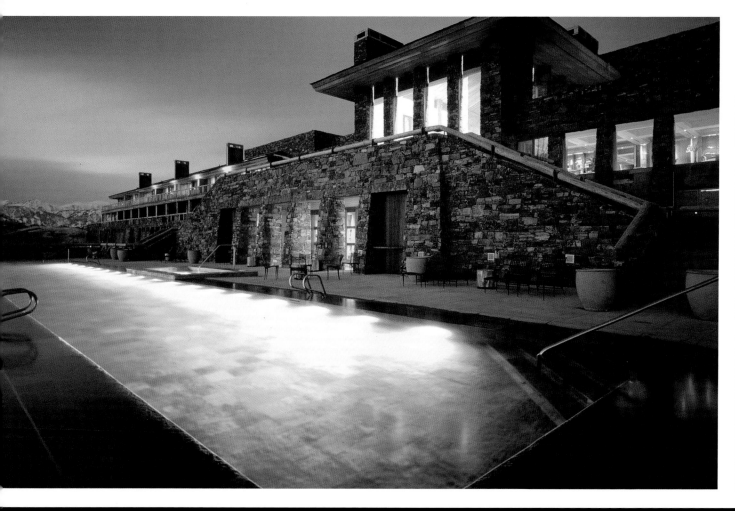

Amangani

Amangani is not only North America's only Amanresort; it's also extraordinarily well placed for adventure-seekers in winter, fall, spring or summer. Located in Jackson Hole, Wyoming, you've got downhill, cross-country and heli-skiing. In summer, enjoy hiking, kayaking, canoeing, horseback riding, mountain biking, golf and flyfishing. The drama of the wilderness will blow your mind. The three-floor, 40-suite resort is backed by the snowcapped Grand Tetons. The quartzite-tiled pool drops off the edge and provides exceptional views over the valley to the Snake River Range. At 27°C, you can use it year-round. There's a gym with redwood exercise studios, spa and black slate steam rooms. The Grill is good for steaks, seafood and regionally-produced organic foods.

QUINTESSENTIALLY INSIDER

Only 20 minutes from Jackson Hole Mountain Resort, Amangani is the luxe ski lodge par excellence. You've got your own fully serviced, private Ski Lounge located by the Bridger Gondola. Book your ski teacher/guide ahead of arrival, through Amangani.

Amangani
1535 North East Butte Road
Jackson
Wyoming 83001
United States of America

Tel: +1 307 734 7333
Fax: +1 307 734 7332
Email: amangani@amanresorts.com
Web: www.amanresorts.com

Bryant Park HOTEL

The name, Bryant Park Hotel, says all you need to know. Location, location, location. This contemporary Manhattan gem has got it in bucketloads, in hip Bryant Park where New York Fashion Week throws its showy shindigs. At 40 West 40th Street, you're in pole position to make the best of Midtown's theatres, cinemas and shops. Yes, Bryant Park is a fine place for a party – there are three suitable venues, including a hi-tech screening room and top floor 1100sq ft loft. Moreover, it's a great place to stay. Twenty-five floors house more than 100 rooms and suites, all with travertine marble bathrooms. The restaurant is an LA import, Koi, featuring Modern Japanese, and the subterranean Cellar Bar an address unto itself.

QUINTESSENTIALLY INSIDER

The 27 Junior Suites and 14 Bryant Park Suites are large for Manhattan – all with Bryant Park views, some with park-facing terraces. Furnishings are by B&B Italia. Forget the 'Ambien'. Room features include a sleep therapy sound machine.

Bryant Park Hotel
40 West 40th Street
New York
NY 10018
United States of America

Tel: +1 212 869 0100
Fax: +1 212 869 4446
Email: cjevas@bryantparkhotel.com
Web: www.bryantparkhotel.com

Hotel Plaza Athenee

The Hotel Plaza Athenee is the Upper East Side perfected: a European-style, 149-room hotel on a tree-lined street tucked between turn-of-the-century residences and Madison Avenue's tony boutiques. The city's biggest and best museums (the Frick, the Met) are within a few minutes walk. The Plaza Athenee isn't trying to be fashionable. It just is, among a quietly rich, knowing clientele who the doormen know by name. Rooms are exactly what you want – everything works like a breeze – in soothing neutrals, enveloping silks, with fresh rose-pink marble bathrooms. Nor do you have to eat out, for Arabelle, the hotel restaurant, is a *Zagat* favourite for modern American cuisine. The bar, amber-lit and leather-floored, serves a mean Martini beloved of residents and locals.

QUINTESSENTIALLY INSIDER

Sure, the Lowell has fireplaces in suites. The Carlyle has elevator attendants. But the Hotel Plaza Athenee is almost unique among Upper East Side addresses: deluxe suites feature outdoor balconies and glass-enclosed atrium terraces – dramatic, cinematic and totally romantic.

Hotel Plaza Athenee, New York
37 East 64th Street
New York
NY 10021
United States of America

Tel: +1 212 734 9100
Fax: +1 212 772 0958
Email: res@plaza-athenee.com
Web: www.plaza-athenee.com

The London NYC

New York City | USA

The London NYC arrived in Midtown Manhattan in fall of 2006 in the former Rihga Royal hotel. David Collins (the designer behind London's Blue Bar and Nobu) has overhauled the look, from oversized guestrooms to lobby and restaurant. The bathrooms are by Waterworks and include exquisite handcut glass tiles, double rain shower heads with luxe details in marble, porcelain and stainless steel. There's also a London NYC Fitness Club. Service is distinguished by a unique feature: Quintessentially. The global concierge company provides on-site assistance for guest requests. Get them to sort a party in the penthouse or in the 2,000 square feet of meeting space. One thing's for sure: at this chic, club-like address you can expect impeccable service to meet modern glamour.

QUINTESSENTIALLY INSIDER

Finally Gordon Ramsay has opened his first restaurant Stateside, Gordon Ramsay at The London. If the chef's tenure at Claridge's is anything to go by, expect this to become one of the three hottest spots in Manhattan (back home in England, the man's got eight Michelin stars in all, including three at his Royal Hospital Road restaurant).

The London NYC
151 West 54th Street
New York
NY 10019
United States of America
Tel: +1 212 307 5000 or 888 LONDNYC
Fax: +1 212 468 8747

Hotel Gansevoort

Hotel Gansevoort hit the jackpot when it opened in 2004 in the heart of Manhattan's oh-so-trendy Meatpacking District. Immediately, the stars flocked in, from Leonardo Di Caprio to Christina Aguilera. They all sought (and still seek) to be a part of the neighbourhood's scene, with its fabulous restaurants that include Pastis, Spice Market, and the Gansevoort's 300-seat indoor-outdoor restaurant-bar Ono. There's also the local retail therapy, including flagships from Stella McCartney and Alexander McQueen. Plus there's the Gansevoort's rooftop pool (unbeatable). Design-wise, expect a cool, masculine mix of chocolates and whites with glass-sheathed balconies and projecting bay windows. The look is at its best in the two corner suites on each floor (where Q has enjoyed many a well-slept night).

QUINTESSENTIALLY INSIDER

If you can push to the Duplex Penthouse, do it. This headline suite features a dramatic, two-floor wall of windows offering unobstructed views of the Hudson River. There's a fireplace anchoring a 30" plasma screen as well as a Jacuzzi and office.

Hotel Gansevoort
18 9th Avenue
New York
NY 10014
United States of America
Tel: +1 212 206 6700
Fax: +1 212 255 5858
Email: contact@hotelgansevoort.com
Web: www.hotelgansevoort.com

Las Vegas | USA

With its Tuscan architecture and eight-acre lake, Bellagio surpasses the expectations of Las Vegas visitors. Romance and elegance are emphasized throughout, hence the resort's appeal among those who aren't visiting for gaming only. More than 1000 fountains dance to music and light in front of the property. A vast chandelier dominates the lobby by glass sculptor Dale Chihuly. Stop by the beautiful conservatory which changes presentation with every season. Experience the Gallery of Fine art in an unrivaled setting. Sleep well in your elegant Bellagio room or suite. Unwind in the new Zen-influenced 65,000sq ft Spa & Salon. Stroll Via Bellagio and browse through timeless designer collections. The restaurants are culinary theatre. Bellagio houses two restaurants awarded the AAA Five Diamond award for three consecutive years.

QUINTESSENTIALLY INSIDER

This is an absolute must for any guest: Bellagio's world-renowned Cirque du Soleil "O" show with its fusion of circus acts, modern theatrical effects, live music, dance, and most of all, water.

Bellagio Las Vegas
3600 Las Vegas Boulevard South
Las Vegas, NV 89109
United States of America

Tel: +1 866 406 7171
Web: www.bellagio.com/DQUIN6

Delano

The newly renovated Delano reads like a name call of the world's top tastemakers. The concept is Ian Schrager (ex-Studio 54), the design by Philippe Starck (the man who reinvented the egg cup) and the headline restaurant is by Jeffrey Chodorow and Chef Claude Troisgros (for Asian food, there's Blue Sea, and on the beach there's The Brasserie with its 15ft-long bar). With this pedigree, you know what to expect: a hip Miami beachfront 'urban resort' on the ever popular Collins Avenue. Now more than a decade old, it has retained its reputation with regulars. Perhaps that's because there's nowhere else in Miami Beach where your white Valextra luggage looks quite so at home, where the kids are taken care of, and where somebody is smoothing out your stay while you get on with having fun.

QUINTESSENTIALLY INSIDER

Book the penthouse or duplex poolside bungalow in white and pearl-grey with white marble bathroom and billowing white curtains. Throughout this 195-room hotel, rooms are serene – the perfect retreat from the party that defines Miami Beach.

Delano
1685 Collins Avenue
Miami Beach
Florida 33139
United States of America

Tel: +1 305 672 2000
Fax: +1 305 532 0099
Web: www.morganshotelgroup.com

The Setai

The Setai is Miami's latest scene-stealer with her white sand beach, three pools, 75 guestrooms, 50 suites and Asian-inspired spa (this one is set to beat the local competition hands-down; likewise, the Asian restaurant). Even the in-room amenities are Aqua di Parma (A-lister or otherwise, they know you'll be popping them in your bag on departure). The Setai is an acutely private place that makes you feel serene whatever the stresses of your life. The gardens are an oasis of tropical colour, the service protective. The suites are cooler than most guests' private homes – we're talking all the big players in music, fashion and film – combining black granite and teak with crisp whites. But then The Setai is the summation of a powerful vision, that of Adrian Zecha, the Singaporean founder of Amanresorts.

QUINTESSENTIALLY INSIDER

The 10,000sq ft Penthouse features a rooftop pool and sweeping panoramas of the ocean, beach and Miami skyline. Book it for a money-no-object vacation. Alternatively, it's the SoBe venue par excellence for a private reception.

The Setai
South Beach
2001 Collins Avenue
Miami Beach
Florida 33139
United States of America
Tel: +1 305 520 6000
Fax: +1 305 520 6600
Email: setai@ghmamericas.com
Web: www.setai.com

The Shore Club

Miami Beach | USA

The Shore Club has it all, designed by famed British architect David Chipperfield with landscaping inspired by the Matisse blues of the Jardin Marjorelle in Marrakech (that would be Lagerfeld's ex-pad). Everyone knows it: The Shore Club has redefined Oceanside cool on Miami's South Beach. The landmark Art deco lobby is the calming transition to a labyrinth of garden passageways, alcoves and outdoor 'rooms'. You've got 307 rooms and suites, including seven duplex bungalows, a triplex penthouse (6,000 square feet, a sauna, steam and pool) and a private oceanfront Beach House – second to none in Miami. The Skybar Miami Beach, with its four separate bars set within the deeply sensual tropical gardens, is the premiere spot for South Beach nightlife.

QUINTESSENTIALLY INSIDER

The Shore Club boasts the best Italian restaurant in Miami Beach, called Ago, this LA import occupies a rustic terrace overlooking the beach. On Thursday, Friday and Saturday nights, it's hopping. Nota bene: there's also an outpost of Nobu serving award-winning Japanese-Peruvian cuisine.

The Shore Club
1901 Collins Avenue
Miami Beach
Florida 33139
United States of America
Tel: +1 305 695 3100
Fax: +1 305 695 3299
Web: www.morganshotelgroup.com

Beverly Wilshire

What a location, at the intersection of Rodeo Drive and Wilshire Boulevard. And what pedigree, this Beverly Hills classic first opening its doors as the Beverly Wilshire Apartment Hotel in 1928. Now known as the Beverly Wilshire, A Four Seasons Hotel, you can expect the best in terms of service. Plus exciting, fashion-forward additions (at a cost of $35 million). These include CUT, the first steak restaurant from Wolfgang Puck (the man from celebrity-studded Spago) with an adjoining lounge sidebar designed by super-architect, Richard Meier. The 8,000sq ft spa has nine treatment rooms, and the pool area (cabanas come with iPods) drips with glamour. Rooms all have 42" plasma TVs and are WiFi enabled. Enjoy, for hotels like this are rare – the progeny of history and Hollywood.

QUINTESSENTIALLY INSIDER

Nine meeting rooms (also great for parties) cover some 25,000 square feet. Together with the location, they have much to do with the hotel's peerless status at the centre of the local social scene.

Beverly Wilshire, A Four Seasons Hotel   Tel: +1 310 275 5200 or +1 800 427 4354
9500 Wilshire Boulevard   Fax: +1 310 274 2851
Beverly Hills   www.fourseasons.com
California 90212
United States of America

Cavas Wine Lodge

Mendoza | Argentina

Finally, a worldclass address to match some of the wines emerging from Argentina. Cavas Wine Lodge, opened September 2005, is located amid the snowcapped Andes and Mendoza's fertile vineyards, a 50-minute drive from Mendoza airport (which is a 75-minute flight from Buenos Aires). This is a place to explore the grape in all her incarnations, visiting local wineries, riding through vineyards, enjoying vinotherapy treatments at the hotel spa. The Restaurant meets the challenge set down by the stunning cellar, focusing on local cuisines and flavours (all ingredients are Argentine). Dishes include rib-eye steak with chimichurri, Andean potatoes and salsa criolla, or baby goat from Malargüe with Incan-style vegetables. There are 14 rooms – all delicious, combining old furniture with modern eclectic artwork.

QUINTESSENTIALLY INSIDER

Don't get hung up on a particular season. Mendoza has a benign year-round climate (hence why the grape thrives so beautifully) and there is always lots to do, including biking and hiking in the Andes.

Cavas Wine Lodge   Tel: +54 261 410 6927
Costa Flores s/n   Email: cecilia@cavaswinelodge.com
Alto Agrelo   Web: www.cavaswinelodge.com
Mendoza
Argentina

Copacabana Palace

It's extraordinary that the Copacabana Palace has remained the Queen of Rio for so long. No other competitor has yet emerged that's even half as glamorous. Just venture down to the pool and find the great and the good sipping caipirinhas on luxe white loungers, taking in the sun of Rio but none of her crowds. Attendants hover with that attention to detail which has made the Orient-Express name (the Copacabana's owners). Sure, you've got a beach on the doorstep, and Rio has some great places to dine. But you'd better believe it: stay here and you won't venture far. There's a gourmet Italian restaurant and a poolside alternative (especially good for seafood). There's a rooftop tennis court, gym and beauty salon (a spa opens in 2007). Even the hotel boutique is a gem. All 225 rooms reflect the 1923 heritage with volumes that would make even the suite-snob smile.

QUINTESSENTIALLY INSIDER

The Pool Suites are unbeatable in Rio: 70 square metres, each with a living room, bathroom and verandah that looks out on to Copacabana Beach. If that's not luxury a-plenty, Pool Suite guests also benefit from express check-in.

Copacabana Palace
Av. Atlântica 1702
Copacabana
Rio de Janeiro
Brazil 22021-001

Tel: +55 21 2548 7070
Fax: +55 21 2235 7330
Email: reservas@copacabanapalace.com.br
Web: www.copacabanapalace.com.br

One&Only PALMILLA

The Los Cabos region of Mexico is having a recherché fashion moment (remember: this was where Hemmingway et al used to hang out, beside the Sea of Cortez). This is largely because of One&Only Palmilla. The resort, opened in 2004, recasts the original 15-room hotel built by the son of Mexico's former President. The new 172-room super-luxe version takes the One&Only vision to a new level, with everything, that's everything, available to those with mullah. There's the Jack Nicklaus-designed 27-hole Palmilla Golf Club, an indoor and outdoor spa, three restaurants, a chapel for weddings, even a customised sewing kit for guests (colours matched to clothes by personal butlers, who also unpack your suitcases). Suites, which are the One&Only standard, are truly vast, all facing the ocean and some with African stone baths.

QUINTESSENTIALLY INSIDER

This is unique: lounging on a floating bed suspended above the Sea of Cortez sheltered by one of the resort's three secluded beach coves. Another don't miss: Charlie Trotter's C Restaurant where Chicago's star chef turns his hand to Mexican seafood. The wine list isn't half bad either.

One&Only Palmilla　　　　Tel: +1 954 809 2726
Carretera Transpeninsular　Fax: +11 52 624 146 7001
San Jose Del Cabo　　　　Email: reservations@oneandonlyresorts.com
23400 Mexico　　　　　　Web: www.oneandonlypalmilla.com

Caribbean

The Abaco Club ON WINDING BAY

Abaco | Bahamas

The Abaco Club on Winding Bay is the latest baby from Peter de Savary, the man who turned Skibo Castle (where Madonna got wed) into Scotland's most exclusive sporting retreat. His new project in the Bahamas is just 50 minutes from Miami, Fort Lauderdale and West Palm Beach. It's 30 minutes from Nassau, located on Great Abaco Island. The pièce de resistance is the world's first Scottish-style, 18-hole tropical links course. You've also got some of the world's best game fishing. Family beach life doesn't come better with more than two miles of beach. Take a 650sq ft cabana, or a two-, three- or four-bedroom Cottage residence with up to 1000 square feet of decking.

QUINTESSENTIALLY INSIDER

Book her into the spa, the kids into the kids' club, and go get some golf tuition with Kenny Gargiulo, Golf Professional. It's top-of-the-range, Abaco's golf course attracting the likes of Sean Connery and pro golfer Ernie Els.

The Abaco Club on Winding Bay
P.O. Box AB20571
Marsh Harbour
Abaco
Bahamas

Tel: +1 242 367 0077
Fax: +1 242 367 2930
Email: reservations@theabacoclub.com
Web: www.theabacoclub.com

Necker Island

It's no secret who owns Necker: Sir Richard Branson. So if it's good enough for him – and let's face it, this man has been around the world and back again – then you're looking at the crème in private islands. Located in the BVIs, Necker comprises 74 acres encircled by coral reefs and white beaches. Between The Great House and five Balinese-style villas, Necker sleeps 28. Take the island on an exclusive basis, or room by room during specific weeks. Eat what you like. Necker comes with great chefs (for anything from roast lobster to a traditional English roast – the guests decide) as well as a stunning wine cellar (like Q says, if it's good enough for Branson...). It's your own private resort with comprehensive staff (including massage therapists) and every possible watersport.

QUINTESSENTIALLY INSIDER

Necker is a supersonic corporate venue that will more than wow the best of the Forbes 500. Then again, it's just as good a place for a 21st, 30th, 50th, 60th or 80th birthday party. Or even a totally extravagant honeymoon.

Necker Island   Tel: + 44 208 600 0430
P.O. Box 1091   Fax: + 44 208 600 0431
The Valley   Email: enquiries@limitededition.virgin.co.uk
Virgin Gorda   Web: www.virgin.com/limitededition
British Virgin Islands

Laluna

When Laluna first opened on Grenada, it got the fashion world excited. For the first time, here was a style-rich hotel in a part of the world too-long afflicted by Caribbean chintz and tacky bamboo. The brainchild of an Italian (ex-fashion, of course), the all-cottage beachside retreat combines Indonesian with European minimalist motifs (for a litmus, one of Laluna's people designed Armani's pad on Pantelleria). There are 16 one-bedroom cottages – well spaced beside the beach and on a wooded hillside to maximise privacy and ocean views. The beachside cottage has a private lawn. Each has a verandah and plunge pool as well as a Balinese four-poster bed enveloped in cottons. Bathrooms are blissfully airy and in part open to the sky. To finish it all off, there is a resident yogi and Sicilian chef.

QUINTESSENTIALLY INSIDER

Don't think you need to operate to somebody else's timetable. At Laluna, nobody questions breakfast at 2pm. You only have to ask and staff make it easy, from eating on your terrace to organising a massage in-room.

Laluna
P.O. Box 1500
Morne Rouge
St George's
Grenada
West Indies
Tel: +1 473 439 0001
Fax: +1 473 439 0600
Email: info@laluna.com
Web: www.laluna.com

St. Mary | Jamaica

Goldeneye was the former home of novelist Ian Fleming who conceived James Bond. He spent nearly 20 winters at this oceanside address that's now an 18-acre private villa retreat. And wow is it glamorous, located on a seaside bluff on Jamaica's northern coast flanked by a lagoon. Rent it in its entirety or opt for one of the five one- to three-bedroom villas. It has its own sandy beach, a tennis court and waterside gazebo for lazy dining. The food is traditional Jamaican (fruit, seafood, tropical spice), and can be served anywhere (all food and drink is included in the rates). Staffing is first-class while retaining the essence of Jamaica. You don't come here to rush. In fact, leave the mobile behind. The ring would damage Goldeneye's uniquely peaceful spirit.

QUINTESSENTIALLY INSIDER

Goldeneye steeps you in nature. As Fleming described it, he found "blazing sunshine, natural beauty and the most healthy life I could live." So get out there and explore, partaking of both sea and land excursions all available via Goldeneye's staff.

Goldeneye
Oracabessa
St. Mary
Jamaica
West Indies
Tel: +1 876 975 3354 / 1-800-OUTPOST (US & Canada) / 00800 688 76781 (UK)
Fax: +1 876 975 3620
Email: goldeneye@cwjamaica.com
Web: www.islandoutpost.com

Treasure Beach | Jamaica

Jake's encapsulates the charisma of its owner: cool, laid-back, full of quirk and personality. It's off the beaten track, which clearly appeals to the celebrities who quietly hide here from cameras. It's also very good value, for Jake's isn't about flash cash but something altogether more sophisticated. You come to chill out totally, to drink beers with Dougie, the best barman in Jamaica, to feast on fresh grilled lobster – Jake's has a second beachside restaurant that serves delectable pizza – and to sleep long into the day. There are 23 cottages, including two, two-bedroom villas and the new super-chic private villa, Calabash Bay which comes with its own butler. These one-of-a-kind colourful, Jamaican-style cottages are strung along Treasure Beach on the island's unspoilt south coast. It's a two-hour drive from Montego Bay, three hours from Kingston, and 90 minutes from Negril.

QUINTESSENTIALLY INSIDER

Book Treasure Cot, the two-bed cottage on the beach where Alex Haley wrote the cult classic, *Roots*. It's also a good option for families, who come to Jake's to escape the 'kids' club syndrome' of Jamaica's all-inclusive resorts.

Jake's
Calabash Bay
Treasure Beach
St. Elizabeth
Jamaica
West Indies
Tel: +1 876 965 3000 / 1-800-OUTPOST (US & Canada) / 00800 688 76781 (UK)
Fax: +1 876 965 0552
Email: jakes@cwjamaica.com
Web: www.islandoutpost.com

Montego Bay | Jamaica

Round Hill is the dowager of Jamaican hotels – all class without having to shout about her pedigree or style. The same clients return knowing she'll deliver. Occupying a former 110-acre pineapple, all-spice and coconut plantation, this is tropical beach chic perfected. Ralph Lauren has designed the accommodation including 36 newly renovated oceanfront rooms in the Pineapple House Hotel with white stone floors, four-poster mahogany-stained bamboo beds, deep tubs and rain showers. This is in addition to 27 villas featuring 74 suites (see our Q Insider). The Elemis Spa, private bay, watersports, tennis, yoga and Pilates all conspire to fill your hours when you're not eating delectable Jamaican lobster on the seaside terrace (chef Trevor Duncan has much to do with Round Hill's reputation) or hanging out with friends beside the infinity-edge pool.

QUINTESSENTIALLY INSIDER

The Pineapple Suites are a catch. Renovated over the past few years, they retain the original Jamaican style. These are Round Hill's most spacious room category with the largest living areas, bathrooms and pools.

Round Hill Hotel and Villas
P.O. Box 64
Montego Bay
Jamaica
West Indies
Tel: +1 876 956 7050
Fax: +1 876 956 7505
Email: reservations@roundhilljamaica.com
Web: www.roundhilljamaicacom

Jamaica Inn

St. Ann | Jamaica

Jamaica Inn has held its reputation as one of the Caribbean's top resorts since 1950. This is largely because it occupies one of the island's best private beaches – 700ft long in a protected marine park – in Ochos Rios on the island's north coast. It has also resisted the temptation to build more rooms and crowd the six acre site. There are just 47 suites, which allows the resort to retain levels of intimacy and accurate service that keep it at the top of everybody's wish-list. The sensibility is quietly glamorous (gentlemen are asked to wear a collared shirt and trousers after 7pm in the main bar and restaurant – you get the gist) and there are no in-room televisions. Watersports and the KiYara Ocean Spa provide distraction a-plenty. Otherwise just kick back, relax and eat like a king.

QUINTESSENTIALLY INSIDER

Cottages 3 and 4 are ever-beloved of regulars. They are situated on a bluff overlooking the sea with panoramic views. Q's favourite is the classic White Suite featuring a wraparound terrace, private pool, garden and jetty with a lounge chair for two.

Jamaica Inn
P.O. Box 1
Main Street
St. Ann
Jamaica
West Indies

Tel: +1 876 974 2514
Email: reservations@jamaicainn.com
Web: www.jamaicainn.com

Strawberry Hill

St. Andrew | Jamaica

Strawberry Hill encapsulates Jamaica's easy-going spirit, a retreat in the dreamy Blue Mountains atop a 50-acre peak. Below the staggering, infinity-edge pool glitters the island's capital, Kingston, framed by an amphitheatre of hills and backed by Caribbean blue. There's no noise – nothing – except for birdsong and the clink of glasses at night. Each of the 12 wooden cottages are spaced through the tropical gardens to make you feel like you're the only ones in paradise. Enjoy a late breakfast on your balcony for you won't see a soul. Furnishings are fresh, colonial-style with four-posters wrapped in cotton nets (Q favourites include Bamboo, Gong, Tree and Cedar). The food is modern Jamaican, using local fruits and flavours in unique combinations created with light, innovative techniques.

QUINTESSENTIALLY INSIDER

Strawberry Hill has one of the best spas in the Caribbean – an AVEDA® Concept Spa offering everything from yoga to holistic body treatments. Frankly, there's no nicer place on the island to see the new day in with a sun salutation.

Strawberry Hill Tel: +1 876 944 8400 / 1-800-OUTPOST (US & Canada) or 00800 688 76781 (UK)
New Castle Road Fax: +1 876 944 8408
Irish Town Email: strawberry@cwjamaica.com
St. Andrew Web: www.islandoutpost.com
Jamaica
West Indies

The Caves

Negril | Jamaica

The location of The Caves is hard to beat even in waterfall-rich, jungle-clad Jamaica. It's perched above Negril's volcanic-formed caves overlooking the Caribbean Sea. Ergo: a hot tub in a cave, a cliffside Jacuzzi, a natural cave for dining. Nearly all of the 10 handcrafted wood and stone, thatch-roofed cottages steal a view of the water; all feel private, for they share two acres of richly-planted gardens, each with its own unique nook or sundeck. Some have outdoor showers and others have verandahs. There's also an AVEDA® Spa. For those who like quiet, but by day three might go stir-crazy, know that the bustling strip of Negril with its nightlife and beaches is just a seven-minute drive away. You've got the best of both worlds, as they say.

QUINTESSENTIALLY INSIDER

There are many naturally occurring holes in the volcanic cliffs around the caves. The largest hole is 20 feet in diameter and located beside the aptly named Blue Hole one bedroom suite. Adventurous honeymooners can take the plunge, literally.

The Caves
P.O. Box 3113
Light House Road
Negril
Jamaica
Tel: +1 876 957 0270 / 1-800-OUTPOST (US & Canada) or 00800 688 76781 (UK)
Fax: +1 876 957 4930
Email: thecaves@cwjamaica.com
Web: www.islandoutpost.com

Turks and Caicos | West Indies

Amanyara is Amanresorts' latest, and the first to have opened in the Caribbean. They picked their spot well, in the Turks and Caicos Islands. You've got some of the region's most exciting diving, powder-white beaches and electric blue sea. The 40 timber-shingled pavilions, contemporarily-styled with sand-coloured terrazzo and pretty teak inlays, are sited by ponds or along the oceanfront. The bathrooms, concealed behind decorative wooden screens, feature freestanding bathtubs and ottomans. What Q likes best are the terraces (each suite has three) with day beds, twin banquettes for dining and lounging, and a third with a sunken table crowded with bolsters. Spa therapists come to you. However, there are a few lures to leave the fiefdom: the 50-metre main pool and the restaurant serving excellent Asian and Mediterranean food.

QUINTESSENTIALLY INSIDER

Just 180 metres offshore lie the dramatic coral reef walls belonging to the islands' Northwest Point Marine National Park – extensions of Amanyara's unusual rocky outcroppings. With almost non-existent sea traffic, it's a great place to learn to dive.

Amanyara
Northwest Point
Providenciales
Turks and Caicos Islands
West Indies
Tel: +1 649 941 8133
Fax: +1 649 941 8132
Email: amanyara@amanresorts.com
Web: www.amanresorts.com

"We live in a wonderful world that is full of beauty, charm and adventure. There is no end to the adventures we can have if only we seek them with our eyes open."

Jawaharal Nehru

ACKNOWLEDGEMENTS

 This book would not be complete without taking time to express thanks to a few people. Firstly, Jenna Bromage. She has put an immense amount of work into the project, and without her outstanding drive and organisation, this book may not have made it to the printers. To the Quintessentially design team, especially Shaun Stilwell who conceived the publication's look. To the Quintessentially travel team, especially Jeremy Sutton and Penny Fieldgate, for their advice, recommendations and contacts. And to everyone in the Quintessentially offices worldwide for entertaining me on my travels, as well as the whole of the Quintessentially London team, for their support and feedback. Finally, to Sarah MacDonald, for possessing such inexhaustible patience with me.

QUINTESSENTIALLY

Quintessentially - the world's leading private members' club and concierge service - is your vital link to the very best hotels, clubs, gyms, spas and restaurants across the globe. With offices and fixers in almost every major city, a membership to Quintessentially keeps you on the inside track 24 hours a day, 365 days a year.

Quintessentially's dedicated travel team only work with the best tour operators, the finest hotels and the most individual properties, tailoring every journey to the needs and tastes of each member.

www.quintessentially.com

LONDON | DUBLIN | CANNES | OSLO | HELSINKI | COPENHAGEN | STOCKHOLM | NEW YORK | MIAMI | LOS ANGELES
DUBAI | BEIRUT | ISTANBUL | KUWAIT | MOSCOW | CAPE TOWN | JOHANNESBURG | HONG KONG